Canadian Mathematics

PROBLEMS
PROBLEMS
PROBLEMS
VOLUME 5

Canadian Mathematics Competition
Faculty of Mathematics
University of Waterloo
Waterloo, Ontario, Canada
1992

Published by
Waterloo Mathematics Foundation
University of Waterloo
Waterloo, Ontario, Canada
N2L 3G1

Telephone: (519) 885-1211, extension 3030
Fax: (519) 746-6592

Canadian Cataloguing in Publication Data

Main entry under title:

Problems, problems, problems

"Canadian Mathematics Competition".
ISBN 0-921418-05-1 (v. 5)

1. Mathematics--Examinations, questions, etc.
I. Waterloo Mathematics Foundation. II. Canadian
Mathematics Competition.

QA139.P69 1988   510'.76   C88-090190-X

Printed by Graphic Services, University of Waterloo

Introduction

Problems, Problems, Problems, Volume 5 is the fifth in a series of Problems Books compiled by the Canadian Mathematics Competition. The aim of the series is to provide a resource that makes it possible for all students to experience the satisfaction of problem solving.

The focus in this fifth volume is on topics that parallel the senior high school mathematics curriculum. The book is a companion to Volume 3 and, as a set, the two volumes provide the variety and quantity of problems so essential to the process of becoming a problem solver.

The questions have been selected from previous Canadian Mathematics Competition contests and have been organized by topic and ordered by degree of difficulty within each topic. This facilitates the integration of problem solving with the day by day development of the school curriculum. All problems are presented in a format that requires full written solutions.

Solving these problems is also an excellent preparation for writing mathematics contests. In particular, it is recommended that students use Volume 5A (without solutions). It is very difficult to become a problem solver when one has immediate access to the solutions. The thrill of victory is so much more exhilarating if one has first experienced the agony of defeat.

We wish to thank those who assisted in the production of this book. Many teachers worked on the committees that produced the problems. Members of the Canadian Mathematics Competition Executive: Ed Anderson, Lloyd Auckland, Larry Davidson, Ron Dunkley, Barry Ferguson, and Ron Scoins prepared the manuscript. Ruth Bradford provided valuable comments when proofreading the material. Members of the Canadian Mathematics Competition staff: Betty Weber, Bonnie Findlay, and Joanne Kursikowski all contributed. In particular we wish to thank Bonnie Findlay for the excellent work she did in drawing the diagrams and typesetting the manuscript. We also acknowledge the generous support of the University of Waterloo and our corporate sponsors.

The organizers of the Canadian Mathematics Competition applaud the many teachers who, through their interest and encouragement, develop a desire among their students for enrichment in mathematics. We hope this latest problems book will provide further opportunities for students and teachers to experience the joy of mathematics.

Canadian Mathematics Competition
Faculty of Mathematics
University of Waterloo
Waterloo, Ontario, Canada
April, 1992

Contents

* Topics indicated with a "*" will be continued in a future volume.

Contest References

Each question in the book has been given a reference number of the form "year-contest-question number". For example, 1983-D-10 indicates question 10 from the 1983 Descartes Contest. The contest abbreviations are: D - Descartes (Grade 13/OAC), E - Euclid (Grade 12), F - Fermat (Grade 11), C.I.M.C. - Canadian Invitational Mathematics Challenge (Grade 10 /11).

Questions

The temperature of a point $P(x, y)$ in a plane is given by the expression $x^2 + y^2 - 4x + 2y$. Find the coldest point in the plane and determine its temperature.

Quadratic Functions and Equations - II

1990-E-3(a)

1. Find the product of the roots of the equation $(x - 1)(x - 2) + (x - 2)(x - 5) = 0$.

1979-E-1

2. If S is the sum of the roots of $2x^2 - 3x + 5 = 0$ and P is the product of the roots, find the value of $S - P$.

1987-E-2

3. A parabola has vertex $(4, 3)$ and axis of symmetry parallel to the y-axis. If one x-intercept is 1, find the value of the other x-intercept.

1979-F-26

4. If $ab = k$ and $\dfrac{1}{a^2} + \dfrac{1}{b^2} = m$, find the value of $(a - b)^2$ in terms of m and k.

1963-JMC-29

5. The roots of $x^2 + px + q = 0$ are 5 and –2. What are the values of p and q?

1975-JMC-20

6. If $1 - 5^{2x+3} = 0$, find the value of x.

1991-E-4(a)

7. If the equations $x^2 - 6x + 5 = 0$ and $Ax^2 + Bx + 1 = 0$ have the same roots, find the value of $A + B$.

1981-E-11

8. In the quadratic equation $ax^2 + bx + c = 0$, a, b, and c are positive real numbers and form a geometric sequence. Give a description of the roots of the equation.

1984-E-10

9. If $kx^2 - kx - 6$ is divisible by both $x + 1$ and $x + m$, find the value of m.

1986-F-13

10. If $(3x - 1)(x - 2) = 0$, find the values of $3x - 1$.

1975-JMC-17

11. If $xy = 6$, $yz = 9$, and $zx = 24$, find the value of xyz.

1970-JMC-17

12. Find the possible values of p so that $3x^2 + px + 5$ can be factored as the product of two first degree factors with integer coefficients.

1986-E-10

13. If $(-2, 7)$ is the maximum point for the graph of the function $y = -2x^2 - 4ax + k$, find the value of k.

1990-CIMC-3

14. Solve $(x^2 + 3x + 2)(x^2 + 7x + 12) + (x^2 + 5x - 6) = 0$.

1990-E-6(b)

15. Determine all values of t such that all roots of $t(x - 1)(x - 2) = x$ are real.

1990-F-22

16. Find the number of ordered pairs of integers (x, y) which satisfy the equation
    $x^2 + 6x + y^2 = 4$.

1968-JMC-15

17. If the equations $(x - 2)^2 + (y + 1)^2 = 0$ and $x - y = k$ are both satisfied by the same
    ordered pair of real numbers, find the value of k.

1985-E-1(a)

18. If $x = -\frac{1}{2}$ and $x = 3$ are the roots of the equation $ax^2 + bx - 3 = 0$, find a and b.

1980-E-8

19. If b and c are elements of $\{1, 2, 3, 4, 5\}$, find the number of equations of the form
    $x^2 + bx + c = 0$ which have real roots.

1964-JMC-21

20. Find the roots of $x^2 + \left(a - \frac{1}{a}\right)x - 1 = 0$.

1979-JMC-20

21. The length of the diagonal of a rectangle is shorter than the semi-perimeter by one-third
    of the longer side. Find the ratio of the longer side to the shorter side.

1975-JMC-16

22. If $\left(\frac{2}{x} - \frac{x}{2}\right)^2 = 0$, find the value of x^6.

1979-JMC-29

23. If a, b, and c are real numbers such that $a^2 + b^2 + c^2 = 1$, find the minimum value
    of $ab + bc + ca$.

1967-JMC-26

24. The temperature of a point $P(x, y)$ in a plane is given by the expression
    $x^2 + y^2 - 4x + 2y$. Find the coldest point in the plane and determine its temperature.

1974-JMC-27

25. If $3x^2 + kxy - 2y^2 - 7x + 7y - 6$ is the product of two linear factors with integral
    coefficients, find the value of k.

1987-E-9

26. The circle $(x - 5)^2 + (y - 3)^2 = 25$ intersects the x-axis at points A and B. Find the equations of all parabolas, with vertical axis of symmetry, whose only points in common with the circle are both A and B.

If $f(x) = \dfrac{3x - 7}{x + 1}$ and $g(x)$ is the inverse of $f(x)$, determine the value of $g(2)$.

Functions

1985-E-5

1. If $f(x) = g(x + 1)$ and $g(x) = x^2$, find the value of $f(3)$.

1988-E-3

2. If $f(x + 1) = x^4 - x + 1$, find the value of $f(0)$.

1979-JMC-16

3. If $f(x) = x$ when $x \geq 0$, and $f(x) = -x$ when $x < 0$, find the value of $f(2) - f(-3)$.

1987-E-6

4. If $f(x + 1) = \dfrac{2f(x) + 1}{3}$ and $f(2) = 2$, find the value of $f(1)$.

1989-E-8

5. If $g(x) = 1 - 3x$ and $f[g(x)] = 9x^2 - 6x + 5$, find the value of $f(1)$.

1990-E-2

6. The graph of $y = f(x)$ is given.
    (a) Find the value of x such that $f(x) = 0$.
    (b) Evaluate $f(1) + f(-1)$.
    (c) Sketch the graph of $y = |f(x)|$.
         Label all intercepts.

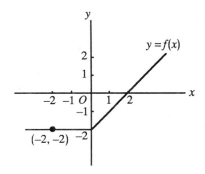

1987-E-8

7. If $f(x) = 5x^2 + ax + b$, where $a \neq b$, and $f(a) = b$ and $f(b) = a$, find the value of $a + b$.

1986-E-7

8. If $f(x) = \begin{cases} 0, \text{ if } x \text{ is a rational number} \\ 1, \text{ if } x \text{ is an irrational number,} \end{cases}$
    find the value of $2f(\sqrt{2}) - 3f[f(\sqrt{2})]$.

1982-E-6

9. If $f(x) = \begin{cases} 1, x > 0 \\ 0, x = 0 \\ -1, x < 0 \end{cases}$, find the value of $f(10) - f(-3)$.

1978-E-6

10. If $f(x) = 4^x$ and $f(x + 2) - f(x + 1) + f(x) = k\,f(x)$, find the value of k.

1991-E-7(a)

11. If $2x = t + \sqrt{t^2 + 4}$, and $3y = t - \sqrt{t^2 + 4}$, evaluate y when $x = \frac{2}{3}$.

1988-E-11

12. If $f(x) = x^2 - 2x$, find the sum of all values of x for which $f(x) = f[f(x)]$.

1976-E-10

13. If $f, g, h,$ and k are functions, and a and b are numbers such that
    $f(x) = (x - 1)g(x) + 3 = (x + 1)h(x) + 1 = (x^2 - 1)k(x) = ax + b$ for all x, find the
    values of a and b.

1989-CIMC-4

14. A function f is defined for integers a and b as follows:
$f(ab) = f(a)f(b) - f(a + b) + 1989$, where either a or b is 1, and $f(1) = 2$.
    (a) Prove that $f(n) = f(n - 1) + 1989$.
    (b) Determine the value of $f(2001)$.

1979-E-6

15. If x and y are real numbers, find the minimum value of the function
$f(x, y) = 4x^2 + y^2 - 4x + 6y + 3$.

1986-F-25

16. If $f(x) = 3x^2 - 2x + 5$ and $f[g(x)] = 12x^4 + 56x^2 + 70$, find all possible values for the sum of the coefficients of $g(x)$.

1972-JMC-30

17. If $f(x - y) = f(x) \cdot f(y)$ for all x and y, and $f(x)$ never equals zero, find the value of $f(3)$.

1980-JMC-29

18. Let f be a real-valued function such that $f(m + n) = f(m) \cdot f(n)$. If $f(4) = 256$ and $f(k) = 0.0625$, find the value of k.

1986-E-9

19. If $f(x) = \dfrac{3x - 7}{x + 1}$ and $g(x)$ is the inverse of $f(x)$, determine the value of $g(2)$.

1985-E-12

20. For every pair of numbers a and b, the function f satisfies $b^2 f(a) = a^2 f(b)$. If $f(2) \neq 0$, find the value of $\dfrac{f(5) - f(1)}{f(2)}$.

1982-E-15

21. Find the value of k so that the function defined by $f(x) = \dfrac{x + 5}{x + k}$ will be its own inverse.

1971-D-12

22. Given a function f of a real variable which satisfies the functional equation
$f(x) + xf(1 - x) = 1 + x^2$, for all real x, determine $f(x)$.

1987-D-6(b)

23. Suppose $f(x) = \dfrac{x}{1-x}$.

   Let $g_1(x) = f(x)$
   $g_2(x) = f(f(x))$

   .
   .
   .

   $g_n(x) = f(f \cdot \cdot \cdot (f(x)) \cdot \cdot \cdot)$ [f occurs n times here]

   (i)   Evaluate $g_2(x)$ in terms of x.

   (ii) Prove, using mathematical induction, that $g_n(x) = \dfrac{x}{1-nx}$.

An observer walks along a level road directly towards an elevated object P. At points A, B, and C, in order, the angles of elevation of P are θ, 2θ, and 3θ, respectively. Prove that the ratio $AB:BC$ is greater than 2 and approaches 3 as θ tends to 0.

Trigonometry - II

1991-E-2(b)

1. If θ, 2θ, and 3θ are the angles of a triangle, evaluate $\cos^2\theta + \cos^2 2\theta + \cos^2 3\theta$.

1985-D-1(c)

2. A, B and C are the angles of a triangle. If $\sin A = \frac{1}{2}$ and $\sin B = 1$, find C.

1986-E-6

3. Find the sum of the 51 terms in the series $\sin \frac{\pi}{2} + \sin \frac{2\pi}{2} + \sin \frac{3\pi}{2} + \cdots + \sin \frac{51\pi}{2}$.

1984-E-4

4. A triangle has sides of length 2, 2, and $\sqrt{6} - \sqrt{2}$. Show that each of the equal angles is $75°$.

1989-E-2

5. (a) The graph represents the function
        $y = a \sin b\theta$. Find the values of a
        and b.
    (b) Find $\tan k$, where k is indicated on
        the graph.

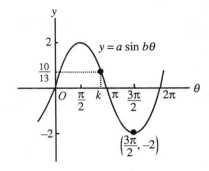

1991-E-2(c)

6. In triangle PQR, determine the length of side QR.

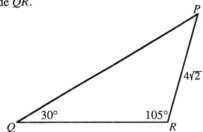

1981-E-12

7. If $0 \leq x \leq 2\pi$, determine the number of roots of $2\sin^3 x - 5\sin^2 x + 2\sin x = 0$.

1987-D-3(a)

8. If $-\frac{\pi}{2} < A < \frac{\pi}{2}$ and $A \neq -\frac{\pi}{4}$, prove that $\dfrac{\sin 2A - \cos 2A + 1}{\sin 2A + \cos 2A + 1} = \tan A$.

1977-D-5(a)

9. If $\tan 2x = \frac{-24}{7}$, where $0° < x < 90°$, find the values of $\sin x$ and $\cos x$.

1990-E-4(a)

10. If $0° < A < 90°$, and $\sin A = 0.1$, find the value of $\log_{10}(\tan A) + \log_{10}(\cos A)$.

1991-E-5(b)

11. If $8 \tan \theta = 3 \cos \theta$, $0 < \theta < \pi$, determine the value of $\sin \theta$.

1990-E-6(a)

12. Find the greatest possible area for an isosceles triangle whose equal sides are each 4 units long.

1980-E-4

13. Find the value of x for which the function $y = -3\cos\left(x - \frac{2\pi}{3}\right)$ has its maximum value in the interval $0 \le x \le 2\pi$.

1987-E-7

14. For $0 \le x \le 2\pi$, find all points of intersection of the graphs of $y = \tan x$ and $y = \sin x$.

1976-E-1

15. Triangle ABC has $\angle B = 30°$, $AB = 150$, and $AC = 50\sqrt{3}$. Determine the length of BC.

1982-D-3(b)

16. If $0 \le \theta \le 2\pi$, find all values of θ such that $\sin 2\theta \le \sin \theta$.

1991-D-4(a)

17. For $0 < \theta < \frac{\pi}{2}$, prove that $1 - \dfrac{\sin^2\theta}{1 + \cot \theta} - \dfrac{\cos^2\theta}{1 + \tan \theta} = \dfrac{\sin 2\theta}{2}$.

1978-D-1(b)

18. Determine an expression for b in terms of a by eliminating x from the following equations:
$$\cos x + \sin x = a$$
$$\cos 2x = b$$

1987-E-8

19. An airplane leaves an aircraft carrier and flies due south at 400 km/h. The carrier proceeds 60° west of north at 32 km/h. If the plane has enough fuel for 5 hours of flying, what is the maximum distance south the pilot can travel, so that the fuel remaining will allow a safe return to the carrier?

1989-D-6

20. Solve $\cos 2\theta = \cos \theta + \sin \theta$ for $0 \le \theta \le 2\pi$.

1991-E-8(a)

21. Find the number of values of x which satisfy the equation $3\pi(1 - \cos x) = 2x$.

1976-D-10

22. In triangle ABC, the angles A, B, and C satisfy the equation $\cos A \cos B + \sin A \sin B \sin C = 1$. Determine all possible values for C.

1973-D-11

23. An observer walks along a level road directly towards an elevated object P. He takes observations at three points A, B, and C, in order, and notes that the angles of elevation of P are θ, 2θ, and 3θ, respectively. Prove that the ratio $AB:BC$ is greater than 2 and approaches 3 as θ tends to 0.

1975-D-10

24. Prove that $\displaystyle\sum_{k=1}^{n} \sin\left(\frac{x}{2}\right)\cos\left(kx\right) = \sin\left(\frac{n}{2}x\right)\cos\left(\frac{n+1}{2}x\right).$

A piece of wire 2 m long is to be cut into two pieces. One piece is bent into a square and the other into a circle. Calculate the radius of the circle if the sum of the areas of the square and the circle is a maximum.

Calculus - II

1. Evaluate:

   (a) $\lim\limits_{x \to 2} \dfrac{x^2 - 4}{x - 2}$.   [1988-D-1(c)]

   (b) Find the slope of the tangent to the curve $y = x \sin x$ at $x = -\pi$.   [1990-D-1(a)]

   (c) If $f(x) = \cos^2 x$, evaluate $f'\left(\dfrac{\pi}{4}\right)$.   [1982-D-1(a)]

   (d) If $f(x) = e^x - e^{-x}$, determine $f'(0)$.   [1986-D-1(a)]

13

1991-D-1

2. (a) State the equations of all horizontal and vertical asymptotes to the graph of
    $$y = \frac{3}{x^2 + 3x}.$$

    (b) The tangent line to the graph of $y = \sqrt{x}$, at the point $P(9, 3)$, intersects the x-axis at Q. Prove that the y-axis bisects PQ.

1982-D-2(b)

3. The radius of a circle is a function of time defined by $r(t) = 4t^2 + 3t + 1$. Determine the rate of change of the area of the circle when $\frac{dr}{dt} = 11$.

1988-D-2

4. A rectangle lies in the first quadrant with one vertex at the origin and two of the sides along the coordinate axes. The fourth vertex lies on the parabola with equation $y = 12 - x^2$. Find the maximum area of such a rectangle, and explain why it is a maximum.

1990-D-5

5. The tangent to the hyperbola $y = \frac{3}{x}$ at the point P in the first quadrant meets the x-axis at A and the y-axis at B. Prove that the area of $\triangle AOB$, where O is the origin, is independent of the position of point P.

1981-D-2

6. A rectangular building is to be constructed with a curtain wall parallel to the front dividing the building into a sales area of 15 000 square feet and a storeroom of 5000 square feet.
    (i)   The outside walls at both sides and across the back will cost $100 per linear foot.
    (ii)   The curtain wall across the store will cost $41 per linear foot.
    (iii) The front wall (mainly glass) will cost $300 per linear foot.
    Calculate the dimensions of the rectangular building which will give the required floor areas at the lowest cost for the walls.

1974-D-4

7. Find all points P on the curve $y = \frac{1}{x^2}$ which have the property that the tangent at P passes through the point $(9, -4)$.

1991-D-3

8. A soup can in the shape of a right circular cylinder is to have a capacity of k cm³, where k is a constant. The material used for the cylindrical wall costs 2¢ per cm² and the material for the top and bottom costs 1¢ per cm². Find the ratio of the height to the radius so that the cost of materials for the can will be a minimum.

1972-D-3

9. Determine the coordinates of a point, other than the origin, on the curve $y = 3x^2 - 2x^3$, the tangent at which passes through $(0, 0)$.

1978-D-3

10. Show that when any positive number is increased by its reciprocal and three times the square of its reciprocal the result is never less than $\frac{13}{4}$.

1970-D-5

11. A closed box is to be constructed so that its length is three times its width, and its total surface area is 30 square feet. Find the dimensions which produce a box of maximum volume.

1979-D-6

12. Two curves are said to be orthogonal at a point of intersection P if the tangents at P are perpendicular. It is known that the curves $f(x) = \dfrac{x-2}{x}$ and $g(x) = \dfrac{x+3}{x^2 - 5x}$ intersect at a point where $x = 1$.
    (a) Determine whether or not these curves are orthogonal at the point where $x = 1$.
    (b) Determine all other points of intersection of f and g.
    (c) State the equation of the tangent line to $y = f(x)$ at any one of the intersections other than at $x = 1$.

1990-D-4

13. The graph of $y = f(x)$ is sketched at the right, for all real x.
    (a) How many inflection points does the graph of $y = f(x)$ have?
    (b) How many solutions are there to the equation $f(x) = -4$?
    (c) Find the equations of all asymptotes to the graph of $g(x) = \dfrac{1}{f(x)}, x \neq 3$.
    (d) For what values of x is $[f(x)]^2 \leq x^2$?

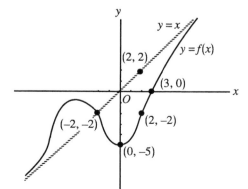

1987-D-4

14. On the same set of axes, sketch the graphs of the functions $f(x) = x$ and
    $g(x) = x + \dfrac{4}{x-2}$.
    Find local minima and maxima, points of inflection and points of intersection of the two graphs, if there are any.

1983-D-2

15. (a) Find any local minimum and maximum points on the graphs of the two functions
    defined by $y = x^3 - 3x + 1$ and $y = x + 1$.
    Find all points of intersection of the two graphs. Use this information to sketch
    the graphs of the two functions on the same set of axes.

    (b) From the graphs in (a) or by other means, find all values of x so that
    $x + 1 > x^3 - 3x + 1$.

1970-D-6

16. Given that the tangent at $A\left(-\frac{1}{2}, \frac{203}{16}\right)$ to the curve $y = 3x^4 + 8x^3 - 6x^2 - 24x + 3$ meets
    the curve again at B and C, determine the quadratic equation whose roots are the
    x-coordinates of the points B and C.

1991-D-8

17. Triangle ABC is equilateral with sides of length 60. At time $t = 0$, a particle P begins
    at A and moves along side AC towards C at a constant rate of 2 units per second. A
    second particle Q begins at the midpoint of BC and moves along BC at a variable rate
    so that the line segment PQ always divides the area of the triangle in half. Determine
    the time at which Q's rate is the same as that of P.

1984-D-10

18. A piece of wire 2 m long is to be cut into two pieces. One piece is bent into a square
    and the other into a circle. Calculate the radius of the circle if the sum of the areas of
    the square and the circle is
    (a) a minimum
    (b) a maximum.

1986-D-8

19. If $k > 0$ is a parameter, determine the maximum value of $f(x) = \dfrac{1}{1+x} + \dfrac{x}{x+k}, x > 0.$

1990-D-8

20. Three squares are shown in the diagram. The largest has side AB of length 1. The others have side AC of length x, and side DE of length y. As D moves along AB, the values of x and y change. Determine the values of x and y for which $x^2 + y^2$ is a minimum. What is this minimum?

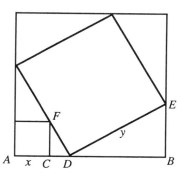

1974-D-12

21. If $f(x+y) = f(x)f(y)$ for all x and y, and if $f(x) = 1 + xg(x)$ where $g(x) \to 1$ as $x \to 0$, prove that $f'(x) = f(x)$ for all x.

1983-D-8

22. Consider the family of conics with equation $4(x-t)^2 + y^2 = 16$, where t can be any positive real number. The distance from any point P on a conic to the origin is PO. For any particular value of t, let $G(t)$ be the greatest value and $L(t)$ be the least value of $(PO)^2$. Determine the value of t which minimizes $G(t) + L(t)$.

The sides of a regular decagon are extended to create a 10-pointed star. Find the sum of the angles at the points of the star.

Euclidean Geometry: Polygons

1986-E-4

1. Given the cube shown, determine the acute angle between line segments AB and BC.

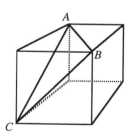

1981-E-1(b)

2. ABC is an isosceles triangle with $AB = AC$. If $BC = 12$ units, and the area of $\triangle ABC$ is 48 square units, find the length of AB.

19

1984-E-1(b)

3. In $\triangle ABC$, $\angle C = 90°$, $AC = 8$, and $AB = 17$. If D is the midpoint of CB, find the area of $\triangle ADB$.

1982-E-11

4. If the corners of a cube are cut off so that a triangle is formed at each corner, find the maximum number of edges in the resulting solid.

1991-E-3(a)

5. In the diagram shown, $\angle ABC = \angle ADE$, $AE = 3$, $AD = 2$, and $EB = 2$. Find the length of DC.

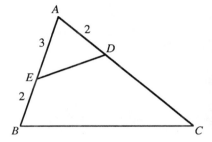

1985-E-6

6. L and M are fixed points, 5 cm apart. Describe the set of all points, P, in the plane, for which the triangle LMP has an area of 20 cm².

1979-E-3

7. P is a point inside a square whose side has length 16. P is equidistant from two adjacent vertices and the side opposite these vertices. Determine this distance.

1990-E-6(a)

8. Find the greatest possible area for an isosceles triangle whose equal sides are each 4 units long.

1984-E-9

9. The sides of a regular decagon are extended to create a 10-pointed star. Find the sum of the angles at the points of the star.

1991-E-6(a)

10. An aquarium is 20 cm wide, 30 cm long, and 15 cm high. The aquarium is tilted along *AB* until the water completely covers the end *ABCD*. At this point, it also covers $\frac{4}{5}$ of the base. Determine the depth of the water, in centimetres, when the aquarium was level.

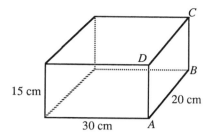

1976-E-1

11. In the diagram, *ABCD* and *EFGH* are similar rectangles. If *DK:KC* = 3:2, find the ratio of the area of rectangle *ABCD* to the area of rectangle *EFGH*.

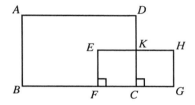

1983-E-7

12. The diagram shows a cube with edge 14 cm. A ball is suspended from the centre point of the upper face of the cube so that the centre of the ball is 6 cm above the base. Find the distance, in cm, from the centre of the ball to the nearest vertex of the cube.

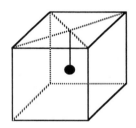

1991-CIMC(10)-2

13. In rectangle *ABCD*, *AD* = 10 and *CD* = 15. *P* is a point inside the rectangle such that *PB* = 9 and *PA* = 12. Calculate the length of *PD*.

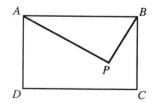

1986-E-12

14. Three squares whose side lengths are integers are placed overlapping as shown in the diagram. If $BC = CD$ and the shaded area is 31, determine the area of the largest square.

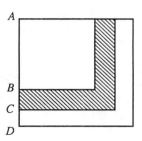

1985-E-8

15. In the diagram, $ABCD$ and $DEFG$ are squares each of area 16. If H is the midpoint of BC and EF, find the total area of $ABHFGD$.

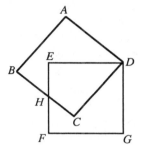

1987-CIMC-3

16. A vertical rectangular post with horizontal top $ABCD$ has $AB = 11$ cm and $BC = 8$ cm. Points P, Q, R, and S are chosen on the post vertically below A, B, C, and D, respectively, so that P, Q, R, and S are coplanar. If $AP = 33$ cm, $BQ = 56$ cm, and $CR = 47$ cm, determine the length of DS.

1981-E-9

17. If four dimes with centres P, Q, R, and S are arranged to touch one another as illustrated, the ***packing density*** is defined as the ratio of the shaded area to the total area of the four dimes. Find the packing density.

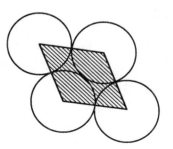

1971-D-1

18. ABC is an arbitrary acute-angled triangle in which AD and BE are altitudes. Prove that triangles ABC and CDE are similar to each other.

1987-CIMC-2

19. $\triangle ABC$ is right-angled at A. The altitude from A meets BC at D, the bisector of $\angle BAC$ meets BC at E, and the median from A meets BC at F. Prove that AE bisects $\angle DAF$.

1975-D-1

20. ABC is an isosceles triangle with $\angle B = \angle C$ and $\angle A = 20°$. Points D and E are located on sides AC and AB, respectively, so that $\angle CBD = 50°$ and $\angle BCE = 40°$. Determine the measure of $\angle BDE$.

1990-E-9

21. In triangle ABC, $AB = 5$, $BC = 6$, and $AC = 7$. Points P and Q are located on AB and AC respectively such that $PA + AQ$ equals half the perimeter of $\triangle ABC$, and the area of $\triangle APQ$ is half the area of $\triangle ABC$. Determine the length of PB correct to one decimal place.

1980-E-3

22. The medians of a right-angled triangle drawn from the vertices of the acute angles have lengths 5 and $2\sqrt{10}$. Find the length of the longest side of the triangle.

1991-CIMC(10)-4

23. Square $ABCD$ has sides of length 12 cm. The centre of the square is O and P, Q, R, S are the midpoints of OA, OB, OC, OD, respectively. Determine the area, in cm^2, common to the two parallelograms $AQCS$ and $BRDP$.

1991-E-7(b)

24. $ABCD$ is a trapezoid with AB parallel to CD. If the length of AD is 12 cm, the length of DC is 5 cm, and angle D is twice angle B, find the length of AB.

1974-D-6

25. AD is a median in $\triangle ABC$ and CEF is a line segment cutting AD at E and AB at F. Prove that $AE : ED = 2AF : FB$.

A vertical line divides the triangle with vertices (0, 0), (9, 0), and (8, 4) into two regions of equal area. Find the equation of the line.

Analytic Geometry: Lines and Polygons

1977-E-2

1. Determine the area of a parallelogram for which three of the vertices are (0, 1), (1, 2), and (2, 1).

1987-E-3

2. The line with equation $2x + y = 0$ is rotated 90° about the origin. Determine the equation of the line in the new position.

1991-E-1(c)

3. The line through the points $A(3, 1)$ and $B(9, -4)$ passes through the point $C(-3, t)$. Find the value of t.

25

1986-E-1(a)

4. If A is a point with coordinates $(4, 2)$, find the equation of the line through A that is perpendicular to the line $y = x$.

1978-E-1

5. $\triangle ABC$ has vertices $A(6, 4)$, $B(4, -3)$, and $C(-2, y)$. If $\angle CBA$ is a right angle, find the value of y.

1984-D-1(d)

6. Determine the coordinates of the point which divides the line segment directed from $A(1, 8)$ to $B(27, -5)$ internally in the ratio 8:5.

1990-E-3(b)

7. Determine the area of the region bounded by the x-axis, and the lines $x = 1$, $x = 5$, and $y = 2x + 1$.

1987-F-14

8. A square has two adjacent vertices at $(0, 3)$ and $(4, 0)$. The remaining two vertices are in the first quadrant. Determine the coordinates of the vertex farthest from the x-axis.

1980-D-1(a)

9. Calculate the coordinates of the foot of the perpendicular from the point $(2, -6)$ to the line $3y - x + 2 = 0$.

1982-F-22

10. If a triangle of area 9 square units is formed by the x-axis and the lines $x = 1$, and $y = mx - 4$, find the value(s) of m, where $m < 0$.

1987-E-7

11. Find the coordinates of all points in the Cartesian plane that are equidistant from the x-axis, the y-axis, and the point $(2, 1)$.

1985-F-21

12. Line l_1 has equation $y = mx + k$.
    Line l_1 crosses the y-axis at P and line l_2 crosses the x-axis at Q. If PQ is perpendicular to both lines, determine the y-intercept of line l_2 in terms of k and m.

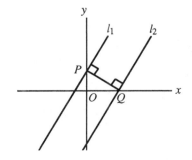

1988-E-5

13. Determine the equation of the set of points in the Cartesian plane equidistant from points $(0, 2)$ and $(4, 0)$.

1985-E-3(a)

14. A vertical line divides the triangle with vertices $(0, 0)$, $(9, 0)$, and $(8, 4)$ into two regions of equal area. Find the equation of the line.

1986-F-15

15. The line with equation $y = 3x + 1$ is reflected in the line with equation $y = 4$. Determine the equation of the reflected line.

1977-D-8

16. A family of straight lines is determined by the condition that the sum of the reciprocals of the x- and y-intercepts is a constant k for each line in the family. Show that all members of the family are concurrent.

1985-F-16

17. The shaded region in the diagram is bounded by the lines whose equations are $3x + 2y = 30$, $2x + 3y = 30$, $x = 0$, and $y = 0$. Determine the area of the region.

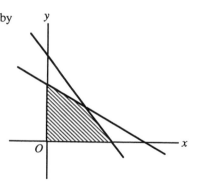

1991-CIMC(10)-5

18. ABC is an isosceles triangle with vertex A at the point $(0, 0)$, vertices B and C on the line $2x + 3y - 13 = 0$ and $\angle BAC = 90°$. Determine the coordinates of B and C.

1988-F-23

19. In triangle *ABC*, medians *AE* and *BD*
    intersect at *F*. If $\angle BAC = \angle AFB = 90°$, and
    $AB = 12$, find the length of *BC*.

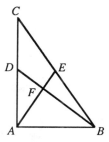

1981-E-8

20. The straight line $2x - 3y + 6 = 0$ is reflected in the line $y = -x$. Find the equation of its
    image.

1991-CIMC(11)-4

21. In square *ABCD*, *O* is the centre. *P*, *Q*, *R*, and *S* are points that divide *OA*, *OB*, *OC*,
    and *OD*, respectively, in the ratio 2:1. Determine the ratio of the area which is
    common to the parallelograms *AQCS* and *BRDP* to the area of the square.

1980-E-7

22. The point $(-1, -2)$ is one vertex of an equilateral triangle having one of its sides on the
    line $x + 2y - 5 = 0$. Find the length of each side of this triangle.

1991-CIMC(11)-5

23. Point *M* is any point on side *CD* of square *ABCD*. Triangle *ABM* is drawn. Squares
    with sides *AM* and *BM* are drawn outside triangle *ABM*. Let *P* and *Q* be the centres
    of these squares. Describe the path of the midpoint of the segment *PQ* as *M* moves
    from *C* to *D*.

1989-F-25

24. Find the area of the region bounded by the graph of $|x| + |x - 2| + |y| = 6$.

1978-E-8

25. Two straight lines are defined by the equation $6x^2 + xy - 2y^2 + 11x + 5y + 3 = 0$.
    Determine the product of the slopes of the two lines.

When $n = 7^{1989}$ is expressed as an integer, what are the last two digits of n?

Properties of Integers

1984-E-4

1. Determine the least positive integer by which 54 can be multiplied so that the product is a perfect square.

1988-E-4

2. Let p, q, and r be consecutive positive integers with $p < q < r$, and let
   $a = p + r$,
   $b = rp$, and
   $c = r - p$.
   Determine which of a, b, c must be even.

1986-CIMC-1

3. Find a base 7 three digit number which has its digits reversed when expressed in base 9.

1988-E-7

4. The sums of 5 numbers a, b, c, d, e, taken in pairs, are 183, 186, 187, 190, 191, 192, 193, 194, 196 and 200. If $a < b < c < d < e$, determine the value of a.

1989-CIMC-1

5. When $n = 7^{1989}$ is expressed as an integer, what are the last two digits in n?

1968-D-1

6. In a certain school, there are two Grade 13 mathematics classes. One class contains m_1 students, and has an average mark of a_1 on a test where the total possible mark is n_1. The other class contains m_2 students, and has an average mark of a_2 on a test where the total possible mark is n_2. Calculate the average percentage mark for Grade 13 mathematics students.

1979-E-5(a)

7. Prove that the square of an odd integer is always of the form $8q + 1$ where q is an integer.

1982-E-9

8. The difference of the squares of two positive integers which differ by 2 is a perfect square, n^2. Determine all values possible for n.

1978-E-4(a)

9. Prove that $n^5 - 5n^3 + 4n$ is divisible by 8 for all positive integers n.

1987-CIMC-4

10. If m and n are any two integers, prove that $mn(m^4 - n^4)$ is always divisible by 30.

1973-D-10

11. Given that p and q are two consecutive odd primes, show that their sum has three or more prime factors.

1982-D-8(a)

12. Suppose m and n are positive integers. For what values of m and n can $m^4 + 4n^4$ be a prime number?

1980-E-10

13. If n is the number of digits in 2^{3217}, determine which of the following intervals contains n:
    (i) $900 \leq n \leq 950$
    (ii) $965 \leq n \leq 990$
    (iii) $1000 \leq n \leq 1050$
    (iv) $1070 \leq n \leq 1075$
    (v) $n > 1075$

1974-D-8

14. Show that, if n is a positive integer, $16^n + 10n - 1$ is divisible by 25.

1968-D-4

15. Prove that the expression $\dfrac{x^5}{5} + \dfrac{x^3}{3} + \dfrac{7x}{15}$ is always an integer for all positive integral values of x.

1987-E-10

16. If $0 < A < 1$, let $x_1, x_2, \ldots, x_n, \ldots$ be the individual digits after the decimal point in the decimal representation of the number A. (i.e. $A = 0. x_1 x_2 x_3 \ldots x_n \ldots$). Let x_1 be even and x_2 be odd. For $n \geq 3$, let x_n be the units digit of $x_{n-1} + x_{n-2}$; (for example, if $x_{n-1} = 7$ and $x_{n-2} = 8$, then $x_{n-1} + x_{n-2} = 15$, and $x_n = 5$). Show that A is rational.

1978-D-9

17. Show that a power of 2 can never be the sum of k consecutive positive integers, $k > 1$.

1990-D-10

18. Determine the smallest integer k such that $60^n + k(71^n)$ is divisible by 1441 for all odd positive integers n.

1978-D-10

19. Show that the product of all prime numbers up to and including a prime p is less than $\left(\dfrac{p + 2}{2}\right)^{p-1}$, $p > 2$.

1979-E-5(b)

20. Prove that the product of three consecutive positive integers cannot be a perfect square.

1971-D-10

21. Prove that there are no positive integers x, y, and z, such that $x^2 + y^2 + z^2 = (xy)^2$.

A death ray, mounted on top of a platform, rotates at a constant speed of one revolution per hour. Every 275 seconds the death ray is fired. Find the smallest value for the total number of times the death ray has been fired when the same spot is hit for a second time.

Miscellaneous Problems

1989-CIMC-3

1. The wheel of a cart rests against a curb as shown in the diagram. Prove that the

   diameter d of the wheel is given by $d = \dfrac{(AT)^2}{AB}$, where AT is the length of the line segment joining A and T.

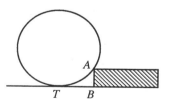

1989-F-19

2. Let $x = m + n$, where m and n are positive integers satisfying the equation $2^6 + m^n = 2^7$. Find the sum of all possible values of x.

1989-F-21

3. Each square unit of polaroid glass will transmit
    L lumens of light. When two circles of
    polaroid glass overlap, no light is transmitted
    through the area of overlap. In the diagram a
    and b are radii and $MN = \dfrac{b}{2}$. Determine how
    much more light the larger circle will transmit
    than the smaller circle.

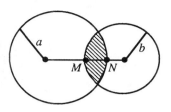

1988-E-7

4. Find the solution to the inequality $(4x^2 - 9)(x - 1) > 0$.

1990-E-7(a)

5. Solve the equation $(x - y + 7)^2 + (x + y - 1)^2 = 0$.

1990-CIMC-1

6. Determine the value of $w + x + y + z$ given that
    $$6w + 2x = 1563$$
    $$2x + 3y + 6z = 4392$$
    $$y - 2w = 1474$$

1983-E-5

7. If $n!$ is defined as the product of the positive integers from 1 to n inclusive, find the
    final digit in the sum $1! + 2! + 3! + 4! + 5! + ... + 12!$.

1988-F-18

8. A network consists of vertices and edges, each
    edge connecting two vertices. The degree of a
    vertex is the number of edges drawn from the
    vertex. (In the example, the degree of each
    vertex is shown in brackets). A particular
    network has 21 edges, 6 vertices of degree 3,
    and k additional vertices of degree 4. Find the
    value of k.

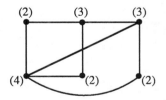

1977-D-1

9. (a)   Identify the curve $x^2 + y^2 - 8x + 6y + 20 = 0$.
    (b)   Show that the point $A(3, -1)$ lies on the curve.
    (c)   Find the equation of the tangent to the curve at point A.

1990-F-20

10. When one kilogram of salt is added to a solution of salt and water, the solution becomes $33\frac{1}{3}\%$ salt by mass. When one kilogram of water is added to the new solution, the resulting solution is 30% salt by mass. Find the percentage of salt in the original solution.

1991-F-20

11. Find the value of
$$(1^2 + 3^2 + 5^2 + \ldots + 99^2) - (2^2 + 4^2 + 6^2 + \ldots + 100^2) + (4 + 8 + 12 + \ldots + 200).$$

1990-CIMC-2

12. A person cashes a cheque at the bank. By mistake, the teller pays the number of cents as dollars and the number of dollars as cents. The person spends $3.50 before noticing the mistake, then on counting the money finds that there is exactly double the amount of the cheque. For what amount was the cheque made out?

1988-F-21

13. The digits 1, 2, 3, 4, 5, and 6 are each used once to compose a six digit number *abcdef*, such that the three digit number *abc* is divisible by 4, *bcd* is divisible by 5, *cde* is divisible by 3, and *def* is divisible by 11. Find the values of *a*, *b*, *c*, and *d*.

1991-CIMC-3(Grade 10)

14. Find all positive integer values of a and b that satisfy the equation $\dfrac{1}{a} + \dfrac{a}{b} + \dfrac{1}{ab} = 1$.

1990-C-22

15. In the diagram, the five marked segments are equal in length. Find the area of the shaded region.

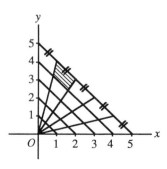

1987-CIMC-5

16. Rectangle $ABCD$ has $AB = 8$ and $BC = 6$. If P, Q, R, and S are any points on the sides AB, BC, CD, and DA, respectively, prove that
$$100 \le (PQ)^2 + (QR)^2 + (RS)^2 + (SP)^2 \le 200.$$

1987-CIMC-1

17. Given the equations $x + y = 30$ and $x^3 + y^3 = 8100$, determine the value of $x^2 + y^2$.

1991-E-6(b)

18. A train engine has a maximum speed of 120 km/h. With cars attached, its maximum speed is diminished by a quantity proportional to the square root of the number of cars. With four cars attached its maximum speed is 90 km/h. Find the largest number of cars it can move.

1990-D-3

19. For the four points $A(0, 0, 0)$, $B(0, 2, 0)$, $C(2, 0, 0)$ and $D(a, b, c)$, let W be the midpoint of AB, X the midpoint of BC, Y the midpoint of CD, and Z the midpoint of DA. Prove that $W, X, Y,$ and Z are coplanar.

1983-E-11

20. Find the number of ordered pairs of the form (x, y) in the solution of the system of equations $|x| + |y| = 8$ and $xy = 12$.

1990-D-6

21. (a)   For what real numbers λ does the system of equations represented by
$$\begin{pmatrix} 1 & 3 \\ 4 & 2 \end{pmatrix}\begin{pmatrix} x \\ y \end{pmatrix} = \lambda\begin{pmatrix} x \\ y \end{pmatrix} \text{ have a solution } \begin{pmatrix} x \\ y \end{pmatrix} \neq \begin{pmatrix} 0 \\ 0 \end{pmatrix}?$$
    (b)   For one of the values of λ determined in part (a), find a solution $\begin{pmatrix} x \\ y \end{pmatrix} \neq \begin{pmatrix} 0 \\ 0 \end{pmatrix}$.

1986-D-5

22. Consider the transformation T: $(x, y) \rightarrow (x + 2y, y)$.
    (a)   Show that under this transformation the image of any straight line is a straight line.
    (b)   When $ABCD$, as shown, is transformed under T, find the area of the resultant figure.

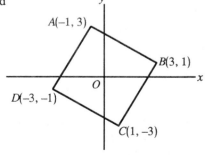

1977-E-5

23. (a) If $M_n = 2^n - 1$ is a prime number, it is called a Mersenne prime. Prove that M_n cannot be a prime if n is a composite integer.

(b) List the first four Mersenne primes.

1982-E-14

24. A death ray is mounted on top of a platform which rotates at a constant speed of one revolution per hour. Every 275 seconds the death ray is fired. Find the smallest value for the total number of times the death ray has been fired when the same spot is hit for a second time.

1989-F-23

25. A floor can be covered with n square tiles. If a smaller tile is used, 76 extra tiles are required. If the dimensions of the tiles and n are integers, find the value of n.

A space-station in the shape of a cube has edges of length s. An astronaut on the outside is anchored at the centre of one face by a rope which allows him to reach a distance s from the anchor point. What surface area of the station is accessible to the astronaut?

Challenge Problems

1986-D-7

1. Four non-zero real numbers a, b, c, d are given.

   (a) If $\dfrac{a}{b} + \dfrac{c}{d} = \dfrac{a+c}{b+d}$, prove that $ac < 0$.

   (b) If $\dfrac{a}{b} + \dfrac{c}{d} = \dfrac{a+c}{b+d} = 0$, prove that $b = d$.

1989-CIMC-5

2. A space-station is in the shape of a cube, each of whose edges is of length s. An astronaut working on the outer surface is anchored by means of a rope which allows him to reach a distance s from the anchor point.
    Calculate the surface area of the station (in terms of s), accessible to the astronaut, if the anchor is located:

    (a)   at one corner of the cube.

    (b)   in the centre of one face.

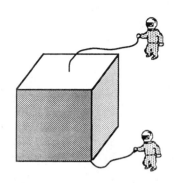

1988-CIMC-3

3. Equation $x^2 - bx + c = 0$ has roots r and r_1, and equation $x^2 + bx + d = 0$ has roots r and r_2 (that is, they have a common root r). Find an equation whose roots are r_1 and r_2, and whose coefficients are in terms of b, c, and d only. Also show that if c and d are positive numbers then b is not a real number.

1976-D-11

4. Given $ax^3 + bx^2y + cxy^2 + dy^3 = 0$ $(ad \neq 0)$, show that this equation represents three straight lines. If two of these lines are perpendicular, prove that $a^2 + ac + bd + d^2 = 0$.

1990-CIMC-4

5. S_1 is the sum of an infinite geometric series with first term a and common ratio r. S_2 is the sum of another infinite geometric series with first term a^2 and common ratio r^2. Similarly, S_3, S_4, S_5, ..., S_n are the sums of the infinite geometric series with first terms a^3, a^4, a^5, ..., a^n and common ratios r^3, r^4, r^5, ..., r^n respectively. If $|r| < 1$ and $|a| > 1$, determine the sum of the infinite series
    $$\frac{1}{S_1} + \frac{1}{S_2} + \frac{1}{S_3} + \dots .$$

1985-E-14

6. Triangle ABC is right-angled at A. The lengths of AB and AC are c and b respectively. Given that the bisector of the right angle meets BC at D, determine the length of AD in terms of b and c.

1971-D-11

7. Let S denote the set of integers 1, 2, 5, 10, 17, ... of the form $x^2 + 1$, where x is an integer. Prove that if k is in S, then k^2 cannot be in S, provided $k > 1$.

1990-CIMC-5

8. All three arcs in the diagram are mutually tangent semicircles on the line AQB. PQ is perpendicular to AB. C and D are the points of intersection of PA and PB respectively with the smaller semicircles. Prove that CD is the common tangent to the two smaller semicircles.

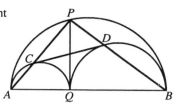

1989-E-8

9. The function $y = \dfrac{a + 3x}{(x - 1)(x + 1)}$ is defined for all real x, $x \neq \pm 1$. Find all values of a such that for any one of these values of a, the range of y is the set of real numbers.

1988-D-10

10. In triangle ABC, $\angle B = 3\angle A$. Prove that $ac^2 = (b^2 - a^2)(b - a)$.

1988-D-8

11. The coefficients of x^{r-1}, x^r, and x^{r+1} in the binomial expansion of $(1 + x)^n$ are three consecutive terms in an arithmetic sequence, where n and r are positive integers.
    (a) Prove that $(n - 2r)^2 = n + 2$.
    (b) Determine all pairs of positive integers n and r which satisfy the equation in (a).

1976-D-12

12. Given integers 1, 2, 3, ..., n, and allowing repeats, we are required to write an ordered sequence with the following properties:
    (i) no two adjacent elements are the same,
    (ii) within the ordered sequence the subsequence ...a...b...a...b... may not appear.
    Example: if $n = 5$, 123524 obeys the properties, but 1235243 does not, since the sequence ...2...3...2...3 occurs.

    (a) Prove that any sequence obeying these rules must contain an element x which appears only once in the sequence.
    (b) Write down such a sequence of length $2n - 1$ in which all elements but one occur more than once.

1988-D-9

13. Let $a_1, a_2, a_3, ..., a_n$ be the numbers 1, 2, 3, ..., n written in any order. Prove that $\displaystyle\sum_{i=1}^{n} |a_i - i|$ is always even.

1990-E-10

14. If x is a real number, $[x]$ is defined to be the greatest integer less than or equal to x (e.g., $[3.6] = 3$). Find all positive values of x such that

$$\frac{1}{[x]} + \frac{1}{[3x]} = x - [x].$$

1981-D-10

15. A partition of a positive integer n is the expression of n as the sum of positive integers, where order does not count; for example, two different partitions of 7 are $7 = 1 + 1 + 1 + 4$ and $7 = 1 + 1 + 1 + 2 + 2$. A partition of n is perfect if every integer from 1 to n inclusive can be written uniquely as the sum of elements of the partition; for example, $7 = 1 + 1 + 1 + 4$ is perfect, while $7 = 1 + 1 + 1 + 2 + 2$ is not. Prove that there is exactly one perfect partition of n if $n + 1$ is a prime number.

1985-D-11

16. Let n be a fixed positive integer. Define, for real x, $S(x) = \sum_{j=0}^{n} \left|2^{j}x - 1\right|$. Find the minimum value of $S(x)$ in terms of n.

1991-D-9

17. In the diagram, P is the midpoint of the line segment AB, $\angle BAC = 60°$, and $\angle ABD = 120°$. X is any point in AC such that XP extended meets BD at Y. Prove that the length of XY is greater than or equal to the length of AB.

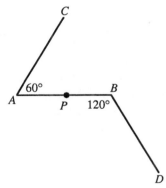

1969-D-10

18. The quantity $f(n, r)$ is defined for n and r non-negative integers by

$$f(n, r) = \sum_{j=0}^{\infty} \binom{n}{j}\binom{n + r - j}{n}.$$

(a) Evaluate $f(3, 2)$.

(b) Prove $f(n, r) = f(r, n)$.

(c) Prove $f(n, n) = \sum_{\alpha=0}^{\infty} \binom{n}{\alpha}\binom{n + \alpha}{\alpha}.$

(d) Prove that $f(a, b) = f(a - 1, b - 1) + f(a, b - 1) + f(a - 1, b)$

1986-E-7

19. In the diagram, points A, B, C, and D are points on a circle in the order shown. If a point E is on the line segment AB, then $\angle DEC$ is less than $180°$. Show that this angle DEC is a maximum *if and only if* $\angle ADE = \angle ECB$.

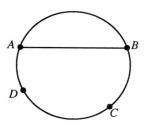

1989-D-10

20. If p and q are positive integers such that
$$\frac{p}{q} = 1 + \frac{1}{2} - \frac{2}{3} + \frac{1}{4} + \frac{1}{5} - \frac{2}{6} + \frac{1}{7} + \frac{1}{8} - \frac{2}{9} + \dots + \frac{1}{478} + \frac{1}{479} - \frac{2}{480}$$
show that p is divisible by 641.

Solutions

Quadratic Functions and Equations - II

1. Solution 1
$$(x-1)(x-2)+(x-2)(x-5)=0$$
$$(x-2)(x-1+x-5)=0$$
$$(x-2)(2x-6)=0$$
$$x=2 \text{ or } x=3$$
The product of the roots is 6.

Solution 2
$$(x-1)(x-2)+(x-2)(x-5)=0$$
$$x^2-3x+2+x^2-7x+10=0$$
$$2x^2-10x+12=0$$
$$x^2-5x+6=0$$
The product of the roots is $\frac{6}{1}=6$.

2. Solution
For the quadratic equation $ax^2+bx+c=0$, the sum of the roots is $-\frac{b}{a}$ and the product of the roots is $\frac{c}{a}$.
Hence, for the given equation, $S-P=\frac{3}{2}-\frac{5}{2}=-1$.

3. Solution
Let a be the other x-intercept.
Since the axis of symmetry has equation $x=4$, then $\frac{a+1}{2}=4$, or $a=7$.

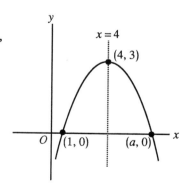

4. Solution
$$\frac{1}{a^2}+\frac{1}{b^2}=\frac{a^2+b^2}{a^2b^2}=m$$

But $a^2 b^2 = k^2$.

Therefore, $a^2 + b^2 = mk^2$.

Thus, $(a - b)^2 = a^2 + b^2 - 2ab$

$$= mk^2 - 2k$$

5. Solution

$$x^2 + px + q = (x - 5)(x + 2)$$
$$= x^2 - 3x - 10$$

Equating coefficients gives $p = -3$ and $q = -10$.

6. Solution

If $1 - 5^{2x+3} = 0$

$$5^{2x+3} = 1$$

Hence, $5^{2x+3} = 5^0$

$$2x + 3 = 0$$
$$x = -\frac{3}{2}$$

7. Solution 1

If $x^2 - 6x + 5 = 0$, then $\frac{x^2}{5} - \frac{6x}{5} + 1 = 0$.

Comparing with $Ax^2 + Bx + 1 = 0$, we have $A = \frac{1}{5}$ and $B = -\frac{6}{5}$.

Hence, $A + B = \frac{1}{5} - \frac{6}{5} = -1$.

Solution 2

From $x^2 - 6x + 5 = 0$, the sum of the roots is 6 and the product of the roots is 5.

From $Ax^2 + Bx + 1 = 0$, the sum of the roots is $-\frac{B}{A}$ and the product of the roots is $\frac{1}{A}$.

Since the equations have the same roots, $-\frac{B}{A} = 6$ and $\frac{1}{A} = 5$.

Hence, $A = \frac{1}{5}$ and substitution gives $B = -\frac{6}{5}$.

Therefore, $A + B = \frac{1}{5} - \frac{6}{5} = -1$.

8. Solution

Since a, b, and c form a geometric sequence, $\frac{b}{a} = \frac{c}{b}$.

Therefore $b^2 = ac$.

The discriminant is $b^2 - 4ac$

$$= b^2 - 4b^2$$
$$= -3b^2$$

Since the discriminant is negative, the roots of the equation are complex numbers.

9. Solution 1

Since $x + 1$ is a factor of $f(x) = kx^2 - kx - 6$, then $f(-1) = k + k - 6 = 0$.

Thus, $k = 3$.

Then $f(x) = 3x^2 - 3x - 6 = 3(x + 1)(x - 2)$.

Hence, $m = -2$.

Solution 2

Since $x + 1$ and $x + m$ are factors of $kx^2 - kx - 6$, the roots of $kx^2 - kx - 6 = 0$ are -1 and $-m$.

The sum of the roots is $-1 - m = \dfrac{-k}{-k} = 1$.

Hence $m = -2$.

10. Solution 1

If $(3x - 1)(x - 2) = 0$, either $3x - 1 = 0$ or $x - 2 = 0$ or both factors are 0.

If $x - 2 = 0$, then $x = 2$ and $3x - 1 = 5$.

The possible values of $3x - 1$ are 0 and 5.

Solution 2

If $(3x - 1)(x - 2) = 0$, then $x = \frac{1}{3}$ or 2.

If $x = \frac{1}{3}$, $3x - 1 = 0$.

If $x = 2$, $3x - 1 = 5$.

11. Solution

Since $xy = 6$, $yz = 9$, and $zx = 24$, then $(xy)(yz)(zx) = 6(9)(24)$.

$x^2 y^2 z^2 = (xyz)^2 = 9(144)$

Thus, $xyz = 36$ or -36.

12. Solution

The factors can only be $(3x + 1)(x + 5)$ or $(-3x - 1)(-x - 5)$

$(3x + 5)(x + 1)$ or $(-3x - 5)(-x - 1)$

$(3x - 1)(x - 5)$ or $(-3x + 1)(-x + 5)$

$(3x - 5)(x - 1)$ or $(-3x + 5)(-x + 1)$

The values of p are 16, 8, -16, -8.

Note that there are 8 factorizations but only four values for p.

13. Solution 1

Completing the square gives $y = -2x^2 - 4ax + k$

$$= -2(x^2 + 2ax + a^2 - a^2) + k$$

$$= -2(x + a)^2 + (2a^2 + k)$$

The maximum point is $(-a, 2a^2 + k) = (-2, 7)$.

Therefore, $a = 2$ and $2a^2 + k = 7$.

Hence, $8 + k = 7$

$\qquad k = -1$

Solution 2

If the graph of $y = -2x^2 - 4ax + k$ is translated $-k$ units vertically, its equation is

$f(x) = -2x^2 - 4ax$.

The x-intercepts of $f(x) = -2x(x + 2a)$ are 0 and $-2a$ and the axis of symmetry of $f(x)$ passes through the midpoint of the line joining $(0, 0)$ and $(-2a, 0)$.

Hence, the axis of symmetry of $f(x)$ is

$x = -a$.

But $f(x)$ has the same axis of symmetry as y, namely $x = -2$, so $a = 2$.

Thus, $y = -2x^2 - 8x + k$

Since $(-2, 7)$ lies on this curve,

$\qquad 7 = -8 + 16 + k$

$\qquad k = -1$

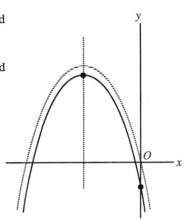

14. Solution 1

$\qquad (x^2 + 3x + 2)(x^2 + 7x + 12) + (x^2 + 5x - 6) = 0$

$\qquad (x + 1)(x + 2)(x + 3)(x + 4) + (x^2 + 5x - 6) = 0$

$\qquad [(x + 1)(x + 4)][(x + 2)(x + 3)] + (x^2 + 5x - 6) = 0$

$\qquad (x^2 + 5x + 4)(x^2 + 5x + 6) + (x^2 + 5x - 6) = 0$

Let $x^2 + 5x = a$.

Hence, $(a + 4)(a + 6) + (a - 6) = 0$

$\qquad\qquad a^2 + 11a + 18 = 0$

$\qquad\qquad (a + 9)(a + 2) = 0$

$\qquad\qquad a = -9 \quad \text{or} \quad a = -2$

Thus, $x^2 + 5x + 9 = 0 \quad$ or $\quad x^2 + 5x + 2 = 0$.

$\qquad x = \dfrac{-5 \pm \sqrt{-11}}{2} \quad$ or $\quad x = \dfrac{-5 \pm \sqrt{17}}{2}$

Solution 2

When expanded, the given equation becomes $x^4 + 10x^3 + 36x^2 + 55x + 18 = 0$.

This fourth degree polynomial factors to give $(x^2 + 5x + 9)(x^2 + 5x + 2) = 0$.

Solving $x^2 + 5x + 9 = 0$ and $x^2 + 5x + 2 = 0$ gives $x = \dfrac{-5 \pm \sqrt{-11}}{2}$ or $x = \dfrac{-5 \pm \sqrt{17}}{2}$.

15. Solution

If $t = 0$, the equation is $x = 0$, and the root is real.

If $t \neq 0$, $t(x - 1)(x - 2) = x$

$$t\left(x^2 - 3x + 2\right) = x$$

$$tx^2 - 3tx + 2t = x$$

$$tx^2 + (-3t - 1)x + 2t = 0$$

For real roots, the discriminant $D \geq 0$.

$$(-3t - 1)^2 - 4(t)(2t) \geq 0$$

$$9t^2 + 6t + 1 - 8t^2 \geq 0$$

$$t^2 + 6t + 1 \geq 0$$

Solving $t^2 + 6t + 1 = 0$

$$t = \frac{-6 \pm \sqrt{32}}{2}$$

$$t = -3 \pm 2\sqrt{2}$$

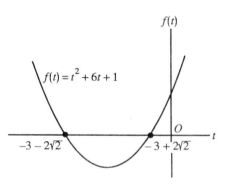

$$f(t) = t^2 + 6t + 1$$

Thus $t^2 + 6t + 1 \geq 0$ for all values of t where the graph is on or above the t-axis. Therefore, all of the roots of the given equation are real for $t \leq -3 - 2\sqrt{2}$ or $t \geq -3 + 2\sqrt{2}$. Note that $t = 0$ is included in this last inequality.

16. Solution

$$x^2 + 6x + y^2 = 4$$

$$\left(x^2 + 6x + 9\right) + y^2 = 4 + 9$$

$$(x + 3)^2 + y^2 = 13$$

$$(x + 3)^2 = 13 - y^2$$

Since $13 - y^2$ must be a perfect square, $y = \pm 2, \pm 3$.

If $y = \pm 2$, $(x + 3)^2 = 9$

$$x + 3 = \pm 3$$

$$x = 0 \text{ or } -6$$

If $y = \pm 3$, $(x + 3)^2 = 4$

$$x + 3 = \pm 2$$

$$x = -1 \text{ or } -5$$

Thus, there are 8 ordered pairs of integers (x, y) which satisfy the equation.

17. Solution

   Since $(x - 2)^2 \geq 0$ and $(y + 1)^2 \geq 0$, then $x - 2 = 0$ and $y + 1 = 0$.
   Hence, $(2, -1)$ is the ordered pair.
   Then $2 - (-1) = k$
   $$k = 3$$

18. Solution 1

   If $x = -\frac{1}{2}$ and $x = 3$ are roots, the equation can be written in the form
   $$\left(x + \tfrac{1}{2}\right)(x - 3) = 0$$
   $$(2x + 1)(x - 3) = 0$$
   $$2x^2 - 5x - 3 = 0$$
   Comparing $2x^2 - 5x - 3$ with $ax^2 + bx - 3$, we get $a = 2$, $b = -5$.

   Solution 2

   The product of the roots of $ax^2 + bx - 3 = 0$ is $\frac{-3}{a}$, and the sum of the roots is $\frac{-b}{a}$.
   Therefore, $\dfrac{-3}{a} = \left(\dfrac{-1}{2}\right)(3)$
   $$a = 2$$
   Also, $\dfrac{-b}{a} = -\dfrac{1}{2} + 3$
   $$\dfrac{-b}{2} = \dfrac{5}{2}$$
   $$b = -5$$
   Thus $a = 2$ and $b = -5$.

19. Solution

   For the equation $ax^2 + bx + c = 0$ to have real roots, $b^2 \geq 4ac$.
   Since $a = 1$, the equation will have real roots if $b^2 \geq 4c$.
   Enumerating all cases for which $b^2 \geq 4c$ gives:

b	c
1	no value
2	1
3	1, 2
4	1, 2, 3, 4
5	1, 2, 3, 4, 5

   Hence, the number of equations having real roots that can be formed is 12.

20. <u>Solution 1</u>

    The factors of $x^2 + \left(a - \frac{1}{a}\right)x - 1$ are $(x + a)\left(x - \frac{1}{a}\right)$.

    Therefore the roots of $x^2 + \left(a - \frac{1}{a}\right)x - 1 = 0$ are $-a$ and $\frac{1}{a}$.

    <u>Solution 2</u>
    The quadratic formula gives

    $$x = \frac{-\left(a - \frac{1}{a}\right) \pm \sqrt{\left(a - \frac{1}{a}\right)^2 + 4}}{2}$$

    $$= \frac{-a + \frac{1}{a} \pm \sqrt{a^2 + 2 + \frac{1}{a^2}}}{2}$$

    $$= \frac{-a + \frac{1}{a} \pm \left(a + \frac{1}{a}\right)}{2}$$

    $$= \frac{\frac{2}{a}}{2} \text{ or } \frac{-2a}{2}$$

    $$= \frac{1}{a} \text{ or } -a$$

    The roots of the equation are $\frac{1}{a}$ and $-a$.

21. <u>Solution</u>

    Let the length of the sides be a and b with $a < b$.

    The length of the diagonal is $\sqrt{a^2 + b^2}$.

    The length of the semi-perimeter is $a + b$.

    We are given that $a + b - \sqrt{a^2 + b^2} = \frac{b}{3}$

    $$\sqrt{a^2 + b^2} = a + \frac{2}{3}b$$

    $$a^2 + b^2 = a^2 + \frac{4}{3}ab + \frac{4}{9}b^2$$

    $$\frac{5b^2}{9} = \frac{4}{3}ab, b \neq 0$$

    $$\frac{5b}{9} = \frac{4}{3}a$$

    $$\frac{b}{a} = \frac{\frac{4}{3}}{\frac{5}{9}} = \frac{12}{5}$$

    The ratio of the longer side to the shorter side is 12:5.

22. Solution 1

$\left(\frac{2}{x}-\frac{x}{2}\right)^2=0$

Thus, $\frac{2}{x}-\frac{x}{2}=0$.

Multiply by $2x$ to obtain $4-x^2=0$.

Therefore $x^2=4$.

Then $x^6=\left(x^2\right)^3=4^3=64$.

Solution 2

$\left(\frac{2}{x}-\frac{x}{2}\right)^2=0$.

Thus, $\left(\frac{4-x^2}{2x}\right)^2=0$

$\left(4-x^2\right)^2=\left(4x^2\right)(0)=0$

$4-x^2=0,$

$x^2=4.$

Hence, $x^6=4^3=64$.

23. Solution

Since $(a+b+c)^2$ is a perfect square, then $(a+b+c)^2\geq0$.

$a^2+b^2+c^2+2(ab+ac+bc)\geq0$

$1+2(ab+ac+bc)\geq0$

$ab+ac+bc\geq-\frac{1}{2}$

The minimum value of $ab+ac+bc$ is $-\frac{1}{2}$.

24. Solution

$x^2+y^2-4x+2y=\left(x^2-4x+4\right)+\left(y^2+2y+1\right)-4-1$

$\qquad\qquad\qquad\quad=(x-2)^2+(y+1)^2-5$

Since $(x-2)^2\geq0$ and $(y+1)^2\geq0$, the least value of this expression is -5 and this occurs when $x=2$ and $y=-1$.

Therefore, the coldest point is $(2,-1)$ and its temperature is -5.

25. Solution

The factors of $3x^2+kxy-2y^2-7x+7y-6$ are of the form

$(3x+Ay+B)(x+Cy+D)$.

If we consider the terms in x only, we obtain $3x^2-7x-6=(3x+2)(x-3)$.

Thus, $B=2$ and $D=-3$.

Now consider the coefficients of y and y^2, using the factors

$(3x + Ay + B)(x + Cy + D)$.

We obtain $AD + BC = 7$ (1)

and $AC = -2$ (2)

Since $B = 2$ and $D = -3$, (1) becomes $-3A + 2C = 7$.   (3)

Solving (2) and (3) for integer values gives $A = -1$ and $C = 2$.

Finally, $k = A + 3C$

$$= -1 + 6$$
$$= 5$$

26. <u>Solution</u>

To get the coordinates of A and B, set

$y = 0$ in $(x - 5)^2 + (y - 3)^2 = 25$.

$$(x - 5)^2 + 9 = 25$$
$$x - 5 = \pm 4$$
$$x = 1 \text{ or } x = 9$$

Therefore, the coordinates of A and B are $(1, 0)$ and $(9, 0)$, respectively.

All parabolas sharing only A and B with the circle have equations of the form $y = a(x - 1)(x - 9)$, $a \neq 0$.

The points of intersection of the circle and parabola can be found by solving the equations

$y = a(x - 1)(x - 9)$ (1)

and $(x - 5)^2 + (y - 3)^2 = 25$ (2)

Substituting (1) into (2) gives $[a(x - 1)(x - 9) - 3]^2 + (x - 5)^2 = 25$

$$[a(x - 1)(x - 9)]^2 - 6a(x - 1)(x - 9) + 9 + x^2 - 10x + 25 = 25$$
$$a^2[(x - 1)(x - 9)]^2 - 6a(x - 1)(x - 9) + (x - 1)(x - 9) = 0$$
$$(x - 1)(x - 9)[a^2(x - 1)(x - 9) - 6a + 1] = 0$$

This is a fourth degree equation which will have four roots.

We want $x = 1$ and $x = 9$ to be the only real roots.

(i) If $a = \frac{1}{6}$, the roots are 1, 1, 9, 9. This situation occurs when the circle and parabola are tangent at A and B.

(ii) If $a^2(x - 1)(x - 9) - 6a + 1 = 0$ has two complex roots, there will be only two distinct real roots $x = 1$ and $x = 9$.

$$a^2(x - 1)(x - 9) - 6a + 1 = 0$$
$$a^2(x^2 - 10x + 9) - 6a + 1 = 0$$
$$a^2x^2 - 10a^2x + (9a^2 - 6a + 1) = 0$$

For complex roots, the discriminant must be negative.

$$100a^4 - 4a^2(9a^2 - 6a + 1) < 0$$
$$4a^2(16a^2 + 6a - 1) < 0$$
$$16a^2 + 6a - 1 < 0$$
$$(8a - 1)(2a + 1) < 0$$

$16a^2 + 6a - 1$ is negative for all values of a between the roots of $16a^2 + 6a - 1 = 0$.

Hence, $-\frac{1}{2} < a < \frac{1}{8}$.

Since $a = 0$ does not yield a parabola, the required parabolas are $y = a(x - 1)(x - 9)$ where $a = \frac{1}{6}$ or $-\frac{1}{2} < a < 0$ or $0 < a < \frac{1}{8}$.

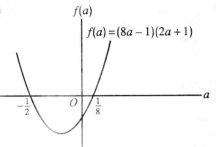

Functions

1. Solution
   $f(3) = g(3 + 1) = g(4)$.
   Since $g(x) = x^2$, then $g(4) = 16$.
   Therefore, $f(3) = 16$.

2. Solution
   To obtain $f(0)$, set $x = -1$.
   $f(0) = f(-1 + 1)$
   $\quad = (-1)^4 - (-1) + 1$
   $\quad = 3$

3. Solution
   Since $2 > 0$, $f(2) = 2$.
   Since $-3 < 0$, $f(-3) = -(-3) = 3$.
   Therefore, $f(2) - f(-3) = 2 - 3 = -1$.

4. Solution
   If $x = 1$, $f(1 + 1) = \dfrac{2f(1) + 1}{3}$.
   $$3f(2) = 2f(1) + 1$$
   $$6 = 2f(1) + 1$$
   Therefore, $f(1) = \frac{5}{2}$.

5. Solution
   To obtain $f(1)$, set $g(x) = 1$.
   $$1 - 3x = 1$$
   $$x = 0$$
   Hence, $f(1) = f[g(0)] = 5$.

6. Solution
   (a) $f(x) = 0$ at the point where the graph crosses the x-axis.
       Thus, $f(x) = 0$ when $x = 2$.
   (b) Since the graph passes through the points $(1, -1)$ and $(-1, -2)$, then
       $f(1) + f(-1) = -1 - 2$
       $\qquad\qquad\quad = -3$

(c) The graph of $y = |f(x)|$ is obtained by
reflecting, in the x-axis, those parts of
the graph of $y = f(x)$ that lie beneath the
x-axis.

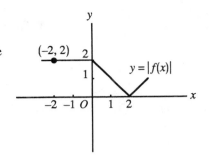

7. Solution

$$f(a) = 5a^2 + a^2 + b = b$$
$$6a^2 + b = b$$
$$6a^2 = 0$$
$$a = 0$$
$$f(b) = 5b^2 + ab + b = a$$
$$5b^2 + b = 0$$
$$b(5b + 1) = 0$$

Therefore, $b = 0$ or $5b + 1 = 0$.
Since $b \neq a, b \neq 0$.
Therefore, $b = -\frac{1}{5}$.
Hence, $a + b = 0 - \frac{1}{5} = -\frac{1}{5}$.

8. Solution

Since $\sqrt{2}$ is irrational and 1 is rational, $f(\sqrt{2}) = 1$ and $f(1) = 0$.
Therefore, $2f(\sqrt{2}) - 3f[f(\sqrt{2})] = 2(1) - 3f(1)$
$$= 2 - 3(0)$$
$$= 2$$

9. Solution

Since $10 > 0, f(10) = 1$.
Since $-3 < 0, f(-3) = -1$.
Therefore, $f(10) - f(-3) = 1 - (-1) = 2$.

10. Solution

$$f(x + 2) - f(x + 1) + f(x) = 4^{x + 2} - 4^{x + 1} + 4^x$$
$$= 4^2(4^x) - 4(4^x) + 4^x$$
$$= 4^x(16 - 4 + 1)$$
$$= 13(4^x)$$

$$= 13f(x)$$

Therefore, $k = 13$.

11. Solution

Since $2x = t + \sqrt{t^2 + 4}$ and $3y = t - \sqrt{t^2 + 4}$,

then $(2x)(3y) = \left(t + \sqrt{t^2 + 4}\right)\left(t - \sqrt{t^2 + 4}\right)$

$\qquad = t^2 - (t^2 + 4)$

$\qquad = -4$

$\qquad 6xy = -4$

$\qquad 3xy = -2$

When $x = \frac{2}{3}$, $3\left(\frac{2}{3}\right)y = -2$, and $y = -1$.

12. Solution

$f[f(x)] = (x^2 - 2x)^2 - 2(x^2 - 2x)$

$\qquad = x^4 - 4x^3 + 2x^2 + 4x$

If $f[f(x)] = f(x)$,

$\qquad x^4 - 4x^3 + 2x^2 + 4x = x^2 - 2x$

$\qquad x^4 - 4x^3 + x^2 + 6x = 0$

$\qquad x(x + 1)(x - 2)(x - 3) = 0$

The roots of the equation are 0, −1, 2, and 3.

The sum of all values of x for which $f(x) = f[f(x)]$ is $0 - 1 + 2 + 3 = 4$.

Note: the sum of the roots of the equation can be obtained directly by taking the negative of the coefficient of x^3 divided by the coefficient of x^4. That is, the sum of the roots is $\frac{-(-4)}{1} = 4$.

13. Solution

$f(x) = (x - 1)\,g(x) + 3 = (x + 1)\,h(x) + 1 = (x^2 - 1)\,k(x) = ax + b$

Therefore, $f(1) = 0 \cdot g(1) + 3 = 0 \cdot k(1) = a + b$

$\qquad\qquad\qquad\qquad a + b = 3, \qquad\qquad (1)$

and $f(-1) = 0 \cdot h(-1) + 1 = -a + b$

$\qquad\qquad\qquad -a + b = 1 \qquad\qquad\qquad (2)$

Solving (1) and (2), we get $a = 1$, $b = 2$.

14. Solution

(a) Set $a = 1$ and $b = n - 1$.

Then $f(n - 1) = f(1)f(n - 1) - f(n) + 1989$

$\qquad f(n - 1) = 2f(n - 1) - f(n) + 1989$

Hence, $f(n) = f(n - 1) + 1989$.

(b)   Since $f(n) - f(n-1) = 1989$, then $f(n)$ is an arithmetic sequence with first term
$f(1) = 2$ and common difference 1989.
Therefore, $f(2001) = 2 + 2000(1989)$
$$= 3\,978\,002$$

15. Solution
By completing squares in terms of x and y, we obtain
$$f(x, y) = \left(4x^2 - 4x + 1\right) + \left(y^2 + 6y + 9\right) + 3 - 1 - 9$$
$$= (2x - 1)^2 + (y + 3)^2 - 7$$
Since $(2x - 1)^2 \geq 0$ for all real x and $(y + 3)^2 \geq 0$ for all real y, the minimum value of
$f(x, y)$ is -7, which occurs when $x = \frac{1}{2}$ and $y = -3$.

16. Solution
The sum of the coefficients of $g(x)$ is obtained by finding $g(1)$.
$$f[g(x)] = 3[g(x)]^2 - 2[g(x)] + 5$$
$$f[g(1)] = 3[g(1)]^2 - 2[g(1)] + 5 = 12 + 56 + 70$$
$$3[g(1)]^2 - 2[g(1)] - 133 = 0$$
This is a quadratic equation in $g(1)$ which can be solved by factoring.
$$[3g(1) + 19][g(1) - 7] = 0$$
$$g(1) = -\tfrac{19}{3} \text{ or } 7$$
Hence the sum of the coefficients of $g(x)$ is $-\frac{19}{3}$ or 7.

17. Solution 1
$f(x - y) = f(x) \cdot f(y)$.
Set $y = \frac{x}{2}$.
Therefore, $f\left(\frac{x}{2}\right) = f(x) \cdot f\left(\frac{x}{2}\right)$.
Since $f\left(\frac{x}{2}\right) \neq 0$, then $f(x) = 1$.
Therefore, $f(3) = 1$.

Solution 2
$f(x - y) = f(x) \cdot f(y)$.
Set $x = 3$ and $y = \frac{3}{2}$.
Therefore, $f\left(\frac{3}{2}\right) = f(3) \cdot f\left(\frac{3}{2}\right)$.
Since $f\left(\frac{3}{2}\right) \neq 0$, $f(3) = 1$.

18. <u>Solution</u>

$f(4) = f(4 + 0) = f(4) \cdot f(0)$. Therefore, $f(0) = 1$.

$f(2) = f(1 + 1) = f(1) \cdot f(1) = [f(1)]^2$. Therefore, $f(2)$ is non-negative.

$f(4) = f(2 + 2) = f(2) \cdot f(2) = [f(2)]^2 = 256$. Therefore, $f(2) = \sqrt{256} = 16$.

$f(0) = f(2 - 2) = f(2) \cdot f(-2) = 1$, so $16f(-2) = 1$, giving $f(-2) = \frac{1}{16} = 0.0625$.

Hence, $k = -2$.

19. <u>Solution 1</u>

If $f(x)$ and $g(x)$ are inverses, then $f[g(x)] = x$ by definition. Hence, $f[g(2)] = 2$.

Therefore, $\dfrac{3g(2) - 7}{g(2) + 1} = 2$, giving $3g(2) - 7 = 2g(2) + 2$.

Therefore, $g(2) = 9$.

<u>Solution 2</u>

If f has defining equation $y = \dfrac{3x - 7}{x + 1}$, then g has defining equation

$$x = \frac{3y - 7}{y + 1}$$
$$xy + x = 3y - 7$$
$$y(x - 3) = -x - 7$$
$$y = \frac{-x - 7}{x - 3}$$

Therefore, $g(x) = \dfrac{-x - 7}{x - 3}$ and $g(2) = \dfrac{-2 - 7}{2 - 3} = 9$.

20. <u>Solution 1</u>

$b^2 f(a) = a^2 f(b)$.

If $b = 1$ and $a = 5$, then $f(5) = 25f(1)$. If $b = 2$ and $a = 1$, then $4f(1) = f(2)$.

Therefore, $\dfrac{f(5) - f(1)}{f(2)} = \dfrac{25f(1) - f(1)}{4f(1)} = \dfrac{24f(1)}{4f(1)} = 6$.

<u>Solution 2</u>

If $b^2 f(a) = a^2 f(b)$, then $\dfrac{f(a)}{f(b)} = \dfrac{a^2}{b^2}$.

Therefore, $\dfrac{f(5) - f(1)}{f(2)} = \dfrac{f(5)}{f(2)} - \dfrac{f(1)}{f(2)} = \dfrac{25}{4} - \dfrac{1}{4} = 6$.

21. <u>Solution 1</u>

If $f(x)$ is its own inverse, by definition $f[f(x)] = x$ for all x in the domain of f.

Therefore, $f[f(0)] = 0$.

But $f(0) = \dfrac{5}{k}$.

Therefore, $f[f(0)] = f\left(\dfrac{5}{k}\right) = \dfrac{\dfrac{5}{k} + 5}{\dfrac{5}{k} + k} = 0$, or equivalently, $\dfrac{5 + 5k}{5 + k^2} = 0$.

Hence, $k = -1$.

Solution 2

If $y = f(x) = \dfrac{x+5}{x+k}$, its inverse, $f^{-1}(x)$, is defined by $x = \dfrac{y+5}{y+k}$.

Hence, $xy + kx = y + 5$, or $y(x-1) = 5 - kx$.

Therefore, $f^{-1}(x) = \dfrac{5 - kx}{x-1}$. Since $f(x) = f^{-1}(x)$, $\dfrac{x+5}{x+k} = \dfrac{5-kx}{x-1}$.

Therefore, $k = -1$.

22. #### Solution

$$f(x) + x\,f(1-x) = 1 + x^2. \tag{1}$$

Since the functional equation holds for all real x, it also holds for the real quantity $1 - x$.

Therefore, $f(1-x) + (1-x)\,f[1 - (1-x)] = 1 + (1-x)^2$

$$f(1-x) + (1-x)\,f(x) = 2 - 2x + x^2 \tag{2}$$

To eliminate $f(1-x)$, multiply equation (2) by x and subtract from equation (1).

$$f(x) + x\,f(1-x) - x\,f(1-x) - x(1-x)\,f(x) = 1 + x^2 - 2x + 2x^2 - x^3$$

$$\left(1 - x + x^2\right)f(x) = 1 - 2x + 3x^2 - x^3$$

Therefore, $f(x) = \dfrac{1 - 2x + 3x^2 - x^3}{1 - x + x^2}$.

23. #### Solution

(i) $g_1(x) = \dfrac{x}{1-x} = f(x)$

$$g_2(x) = f[f(x)] = f[g_1(x)] = \dfrac{\dfrac{x}{1-x}}{1 - \dfrac{x}{1-x}} = \dfrac{x}{1-x-x} = \dfrac{x}{1-2x}.$$

(ii) In part (i), we determined that the formula $g_n(x) = \dfrac{x}{1-nx}$ is valid for $n = 1, 2$.

Assume the formula is true for $n = k$; that is, assume $g_k(x) = \dfrac{x}{1-kx}$.

Since $g_{k+1}(x) = f[g_k(x)]$ by the definition,

$$g_{k+1}(x) = \dfrac{g_k(x)}{1 - g_k(x)} = \dfrac{\dfrac{x}{1-kx}}{1 - \dfrac{x}{1-kx}} = \dfrac{x}{1-kx-x} = \dfrac{x}{1-(k+1)x}.$$

Thus the formula is valid for $n = k + 1$ whenever it is valid for $n = k$ and since it is valid for $n = 1$, it follows, by mathematical induction, that $g_n(x) = \dfrac{x}{1-nx}$

for all positive integers n.

Trigonometry - II

1. Solution
    Since θ, 2θ, and 3θ are the angles of a triangle,
    $$\theta + 2\theta + 3\theta = 180°$$
    $$6\theta = 180°$$
    $$\theta = 30°$$
    Therefore, $\cos^2\theta + \cos^2(2\theta) + \cos^2(3\theta) = \cos^2(30°) + \cos^2(60°) + \cos^2(90°)$
    $$= \left(\frac{\sqrt{3}}{2}\right)^2 + \left(\frac{1}{2}\right)^2 + (0)^2$$
    $$= 1$$

2. Solution
    Since $\sin B = 1$, $B = 90°$.
    Since $\sin A = \frac{1}{2}$, $A = 30°$.
    Hence, $C = 180° - 90° - 30°$
    $$= 60°$$

    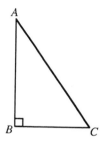

3. Solution

    $\sin \frac{\pi}{2} + \sin \frac{2\pi}{2} + \sin \frac{3\pi}{2} + \cdots + \sin \frac{51\pi}{2}$
    $= 1 + 0 - 1 + 0 + 1 + 0 - 1 + 0 + \cdots + 1 + 0 - 1$,   to 51 terms
    $= (1 + 0 - 1 + 0) + (1 + 0 - 1 + 0) + \cdots + (1 + 0 - 1)$
    $= 0$

4. Solution

    Using the Law of Cosines,

    $$(\sqrt{6} - \sqrt{2})^2 = (2)^2 + (2)^2 - (2)(2)(2)\cos A$$
    $$6 - 2\sqrt{12} + 2 = 8 - 8\cos A$$
    $$\cos A = \frac{\sqrt{3}}{2}$$

    Hence, $A = 30°$.

    Thus, each of the equal angles is

    $$\frac{180° - 30°}{2} = 75°.$$

    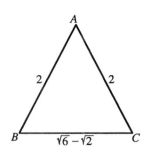

5. Solution

    (a) From the graph, the amplitude is 2
        and the period is 2π.
        Therefore, $a = 2$ and $b = 1$.

    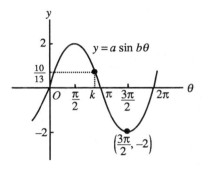

    (b) Since $\left(k, \frac{10}{13}\right)$ is a point on the graph of $y = 2\sin\theta$,

        $$2\sin k = \frac{10}{13}$$
        $$\sin k = \frac{5}{13}$$

        Since $\frac{\pi}{2} < k < \pi$, k is a second quadrant angle.

        In the diagram,

        $$x^2 + 25 = 169$$
        $$x = -12$$

        Thus, $\tan k = -\frac{5}{12}$.

        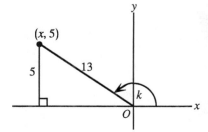

○

6. Solution 1

In $\triangle PQR$, $\angle P = 180° - (30° + 105°) = 45°$.

By the Law of Sines,

$$\frac{4\sqrt{2}}{\sin 30°} = \frac{QR}{\sin 45°}$$

$$\frac{4\sqrt{2}}{\frac{1}{2}} = \frac{QR}{\frac{1}{\sqrt{2}}}$$

$$\frac{1}{2}QR = 4$$

$$QR = 8$$

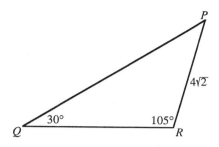

Solution 2

In $\triangle PQR$, $\angle P = 180° - (30° + 105°) = 45°$.

Draw perpendicular RT to side PQ.

Thus $\angle PRT = 45°$.

$\triangle PRT$ is a 45°-45°-90° triangle, and $PR = 4\sqrt{2}$,

so $RT = 4$.

In $\triangle QRT$, $\sin 30° = \dfrac{RT}{QR}$

$$\frac{1}{2} = \frac{4}{QR}$$

$$QR = 8$$

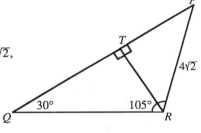

7. Solution

$$2\sin^3 x - 5\sin^2 x + 2\sin x = 0$$

$$\sin x [2\sin^2 x - 5\sin x + 2] = 0$$

$$\sin x (2\sin x - 1)(\sin x - 2) = 0$$

In the given domain;

$\sin x = 0$ for $x = 0, \pi, 2\pi$

$\sin x = \dfrac{1}{2}$ for $x = \dfrac{\pi}{5}, \dfrac{5\pi}{6}$

There are no values of x for which $\sin x = 2$.

The number of roots is five.

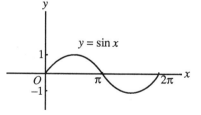

8. Solution

$$\frac{\sin 2a - \cos 2a + 1}{\sin 2a + \cos 2a + 1} = \frac{2\sin A \cos A - (1 - 2\sin^2 A) + 1}{2\sin A \cos A + (2\cos^2 A - 1) + 1}$$

$$= \frac{2\sin A(\cos A + \sin A)}{2\cos A(\sin A + \cos A)}$$

$$= \frac{\sin A}{\cos A}$$

$$= \tan A$$

9. Solution

    Since $0° < x < 90°$ and tan $2x$ is negative, $2x$ is a second quadrant angle.

    In the diagram, $OQ = \sqrt{24^2 + 7^2} = 25$.

    Thus, $\cos 2x = -\frac{7}{25}$

    $2\cos^2 x - 1 = -\frac{7}{25}$

    $\cos^2 x = \frac{9}{25}$

    $\cos x = \frac{3}{5}$

    Hence, $\sin x = \frac{4}{5}$.

    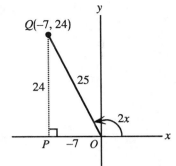

    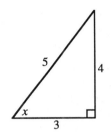

10. Solution

    $\log_{10}(\tan A) + \log_{10}(\cos A) = \log_{10}(\tan A \cos A)$

    $= \log_{10}\left(\frac{\sin A}{\cos A} \cdot \cos A\right)$

    $= \log_{10}(\sin A)$

    $= \log_{10}\left(\frac{1}{10}\right)$

    $= -1$

11. Solution

    $8 \tan \theta = 3 \cos \theta$

    $8 \frac{\sin \theta}{\cos \theta} = 3 \cos \theta$

    $8 \sin \theta = 3 \cos^2\theta$

    $8 \sin \theta = 3(1 - \sin^2\theta)$

    $8 \sin \theta = 3 - 3 \sin^2\theta$

    $3 \sin^2\theta + 8 \sin \theta - 3 = 0$

    $(\sin \theta + 3)(3 \sin \theta - 1) = 0$

    Therefore, $\sin \theta = -3$ or $\sin \theta = \frac{1}{3}$.

But $-1 \le \sin \theta \le 1$, so $\sin \theta \ne -3$.

Therefore, $\sin \theta = \frac{1}{3}$.

12. Solution

Let the angle between the two equal sides be θ.

Draw PS perpendicular to QR.

The area of the triangle is $A = \frac{1}{2}(\text{base})(\text{height})$

$$= \frac{1}{2}(4)(AD)$$

Since $\frac{PS}{4} = \sin \theta$, $PS = 4 \sin \theta$.

Thus, $A = 8 \sin \theta$.

Since $0° < \theta < 180°$, the maximum value of A is 8 and this occurs when $\theta = 90°$.

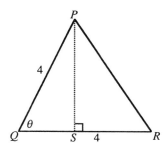

13. Solution

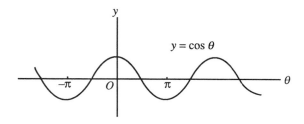

The values of x for which the function $y = -3\cos\left(x - \frac{2\pi}{3}\right)$ attains its maximum values are the same as the values for which the function $y = \cos\left(x - \frac{2\pi}{3}\right)$ attains its minimum values.

The function $y = \cos \theta$ attains minimum values at $\theta = (2k + 1)\pi$ for $k = 0, \pm1, \pm2, \dots$.

Thus, the given function attains its maximum values when $x - \frac{2\pi}{3} = (2k + 1)\pi$.

Therefore, $x = \left(2k + \frac{5}{3}\right)\pi$, for all integers k.

One such value for x is $\frac{5}{3}\pi$, occurring when $k = 0$.

14. Solution

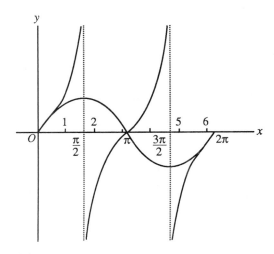

To find the points common to the graphs of $y = \tan x$ and $y = \sin x$, we solve

$$\sin x = \tan x$$

$$\sin x - \frac{\sin x}{\cos x} = 0 \;,\quad \cos x \neq 0$$

$$\frac{\sin x \cos x - \sin x}{\cos x} = 0 \;,\quad \cos x \neq 0$$

Thus, $\sin x(\cos x - 1) = 0$

$$\sin x = 0 \quad \text{or} \quad \cos x = 1$$

The values of x that satisfy these conditions are $x = 0, \pi, 2\pi$.

The graphs intersect at the three points $(0, 0)$, $(\pi, 0)$ and $(2\pi, 0)$.

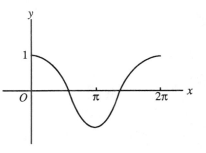

15. Solution

Two triangles are possible, $\triangle ABC$ and $\triangle ABC'$.

Draw $AD \perp CC'$.

In $\triangle ABD$, $\angle BAD = 60°$ and $AD = \frac{1}{2}AB = 75$.

In $\triangle ACD$, $\sin \angle ACD = \dfrac{AD}{AC}$

$$= \frac{75}{50\sqrt{3}}$$

$$= \frac{\sqrt{3}}{2}$$

Hence, $\angle ACD = 60° = \angle AC'D$.

Thus, $CC' = 50\sqrt{3}$.

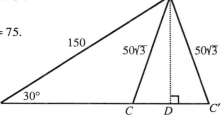

In $\triangle ABC$, $\angle ACB = 120°$.

Hence, $\angle BAC = 30°$ and $BC = 50\sqrt{3}$.

The lengths of BC for the two possible cases are $50\sqrt{3}$ and $100\sqrt{3}$.

16. Solution

A sketch of the graphs of $y = \sin 2\theta$ and $y = \sin \theta$ is shown for $0 \le \theta \le 2\pi$.

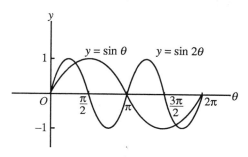

The solution for $\sin 2\theta \le \sin \theta$ is the set of values of θ for which the graph of $y = \sin 2\theta$ is below the graph of $y = \sin \theta$ and the values for which they are equal. To find the points of intersection, we solve

$$\sin 2\theta = \sin \theta$$
$$2 \sin \theta \cos \theta = \sin \theta$$
$$\sin \theta (2 \cos \theta - 1) = 0$$
$$\sin \theta = 0 \quad \text{or} \quad \cos \theta = \tfrac{1}{2}$$

The graphs intersect at $\theta = 0, \frac{\pi}{3}, \pi, \frac{5\pi}{3}, 2\pi$.

Thus, $\sin 2\theta \le \sin \theta$ if $\theta = 0$ or $\frac{\pi}{3} \le \theta \le \pi$ or $\frac{5\pi}{3} \le \theta \le 2\pi$.

17. Solution

$$1 - \frac{\sin^2\theta}{1 + \cot\theta} - \frac{\cos^2\theta}{1 + \tan\theta} = 1 - \frac{\sin^2\theta}{1 + \dfrac{\cos\theta}{\sin\theta}} - \frac{\cos^2\theta}{1 + \dfrac{\sin\theta}{\cos\theta}}$$

$$= 1 - \frac{\sin^3\theta}{\sin\theta + \cos\theta} - \frac{\cos^3\theta}{\sin\theta + \cos\theta}$$

$$= 1 - \frac{\sin^3\theta + \cos^3\theta}{\sin\theta + \cos\theta}$$

$$= 1 - \frac{(\sin\theta + \cos\theta)(\sin^2\theta - \sin\theta\cos\theta + \cos^2\theta)}{\sin\theta + \cos\theta}$$

$$= 1 - (\sin^2\theta + \cos^2\theta - \sin\theta\cos\theta)$$

$$= \sin \theta \cos \theta$$
$$= \frac{\sin 2\theta}{2}$$

18. Solution

    $\cos x + \sin x = a$ (1)

         $\cos 2x = b$ (2)

    Squaring both sides of (1) produces

         $\cos^2 x + 2 \sin x \cos x + \sin^2 x = a^2$

    Thus, $\sin 2x = a^2 - 1$.

    We also know $\sin^2 2x + \cos^2 2x = 1$.

    Thus, $(a^2 - 1)^2 + b^2 = 1$

               $b^2 = 2a^2 - a^4$

    Hence, $b = \pm\sqrt{2a^2 - a^4}$.

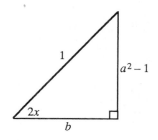

19. Solution

    Let d km be the distance south that the pilot
    can travel, and still have enough fuel
    remaining to return to the carrier.

    In 5 hours, the plane travels 2000 km and
    the carrier travels 160 km.

    In the diagram, $AC = 160$ km, $BC = d$ km,
    $AB = (2000 - d)$ km and $\angle ACB = 120°$.

    By the Law of Cosines,

         $(2000 - d)^2 = 160^2 + d^2 - 2(160)(d)\cos 120°$

         $4\,000\,000 - 4000d + d^2 = 25\,600 + d^2 + 160d$

                    $4160d = 3\,974\,400$

                       $d \approx 955.38$

    Thus, the pilot can travel 955 km south before
    turning back for a safe return to the carrier.

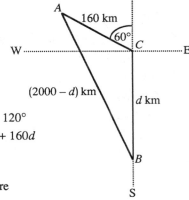

20. Solution 1

    Since $\cos 2\theta = \cos^2\theta - \sin^2\theta$, the equation becomes

                 $\cos^2\theta - \sin^2\theta = \cos\theta + \sin\theta$

    $(\cos\theta - \sin\theta)(\cos\theta + \sin\theta) = \cos\theta + \sin\theta$

    Hence, $\cos\theta + \sin\theta = 0$ (1)

    or $\cos\theta - \sin\theta = 1$ (2)

Equation (1) gives $\sin\theta = -\cos\theta$

$$\tan\theta = -1$$

and so $\theta = \dfrac{3\pi}{4}$ or $\dfrac{7\pi}{4}$ in the given domain.

Upon squaring equation (2), we get $\cos^2\theta - 2\sin\theta\cos\theta + \sin^2\theta = 1$

$$2\sin\theta\cos\theta = 0$$

$$\sin 2\theta = 0$$

Hence, $2\theta = k\pi$ and within the given domain the allowed values of k are 0, 1, 2, 3, 4, giving $\theta = 0, \dfrac{\pi}{2}, \pi, \dfrac{3\pi}{2}, 2\pi$.

Because equation (2) was squared, we must verify that these values satisfy (2). $\dfrac{\pi}{2}$ and π are not solutions of (2).

Therefore, the solutions are $\theta = 0, \dfrac{3\pi}{4}, \dfrac{3\pi}{2}, \dfrac{7\pi}{4}, 2\pi$.

Solution 2

Note that Solution 1 requires checking of answers obtained. This can be avoided if we proceed as follows.

The initial analysis is as in Solution 1.

Equation (2) is $\cos\theta - \sin\theta = 1$.

Hence, $\dfrac{1}{\sqrt{2}}\cos\theta - \dfrac{1}{\sqrt{2}}\sin\theta = \dfrac{1}{\sqrt{2}}$

$$\cos\frac{\pi}{4}\cos\theta - \sin\frac{\pi}{4}\sin\theta = \frac{1}{\sqrt{2}}$$

$$\cos\left(\theta + \frac{\pi}{4}\right) = \frac{1}{\sqrt{2}}$$

$$\theta + \frac{\pi}{4} = \frac{\pi}{4}, \frac{7\pi}{4}, \frac{9\pi}{4}$$

Hence, $\theta = 0, \dfrac{3\pi}{2}, 2\pi$ and together with case (1) we have $\theta = 0, \dfrac{3\pi}{4}, \dfrac{3\pi}{2}, \dfrac{7\pi}{4}, 2\pi$.

21. ### Solution

$$3\pi(1 - \cos x) = 2x$$

$$1 - \cos x = \frac{2}{3\pi}x \qquad (1)$$

To solve (1), consider the graphs of $y = \dfrac{2}{3\pi}x$ and $y = 1 - \cos x$.

The number of solutions to the given equation is the same as the number of points of intersection of the two graphs.

The graph of $y = \dfrac{2}{3\pi}x$ is a straight line with slope $\dfrac{2}{3\pi}$ and passes through the points $(0, 0)$ and $(3\pi, 2)$.

To graph $y = 1 - \cos x$, first draw the graph of $y = \cos x$.

The graph of $y = -\cos x$ is the reflection of the graph of $y = \cos x$ in the x-axis.

Finally, the graph of $y = 1 - \cos x$ is a translation of the graph of $y = -\cos x$ one unit upward.

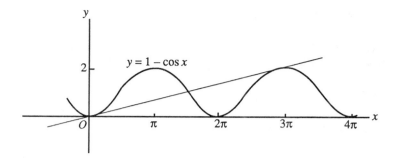

Since the graph of $y = 1 - \cos x$ is never below the x-axis, there are no points of intersection for $x < 0$.

Since the graph of $y = \dfrac{2}{3\pi} x$ is above 2 for all $x > 3\pi$, there are no points of intersection for $x > 3\pi$.

Since $(0, 0)$ and $(3\pi, 2)$ are common to the two graphs and are not points of tangency, there must be neighbouring points of intersection.

Therefore, there are five values of x for which $3\pi(1 - \cos x) = 2x$.

22. <u>Solution</u>

$\cos A \cos B + \sin A \sin B \sin C = 1$

Thus, $\cos A \cos B + \sin A \sin B = 1 + \sin A \sin B(1 - \sin C)$

$\qquad\qquad \cos (A - B) = 1 + \sin A \sin B(1 - \sin C)$ (1)

Since A, B, and C are the angles of a triangle,

$\qquad 0 < \sin A \leq 1, 0 < \sin B \leq 1, 0 < \sin C \leq 1$

The largest value the left hand side of equation (1) can be is 1.

The smallest value the right hand side of equation (1) can be is 1.

For equality, the left hand side and right hand side of equation (1) must be be 1.

This occurs when $\sin C = 1$.

Thus, $C = 90°$.

23. <u>Solution</u>

Since $\angle PBC = \angle PAB + \angle APB = 2\theta$,

then $\angle APB = \theta$.

Thus, $AB = BP$.

Since $\angle PCD = \angle PBC + \angle BPC = 3\theta$,

then $\angle BPC = \theta$.

Also, $\angle PCB = 180° - 3\theta$.

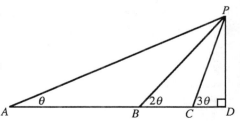

Using the Sine Law in triangle *PBC* yields

$$\frac{BP}{BC} = \frac{\sin\left(180° - 3\theta\right)}{\sin\theta} = \frac{\sin 3\theta}{\sin\theta}$$

Since $\sin 3\theta = \sin\left(2\theta + \theta\right)$

$$= \sin 2\theta\cos\theta + \cos 2\theta\sin\theta$$
$$= 2\sin\theta\cos^2\theta + \left(1 - 2\sin^2\theta\right)\sin\theta$$
$$= 3\sin\theta - 4\sin^3\theta$$

and since $BP = AB$, $\dfrac{AB}{BC} = 3 - 4\sin^2\theta$.

As $\theta \to 0$, $\dfrac{AB}{BC} \to 3$ and $\displaystyle\lim_{\theta \to 0}\left(\frac{AB}{BC}\right) = 3$.

Also, $3\theta < 90°$ and hence $\theta < 30°$.

Thus, $\dfrac{AB}{BC} > 3 - 4\sin^2(30°) = 3 - 4\left(\frac{1}{4}\right) = 2$.

24. Solution 1

This identity can be proved by expressing the products on the left side as sums. Since the right side is a single term, we will express the left side as a series of terms in which the signs alternate, and all but two terms combine in pairs to give zeros.

Since $\sin\left(A + B\right) = \sin A\cos B + \cos A\sin B$

and $\sin\left(A - B\right) = \sin A\cos B - \cos A\sin B$

$\sin\left(A + B\right) - \sin\left(A - B\right) = 2\cos A\sin B$

Thus, $\cos A\sin B = \frac{1}{2}\left[\sin\left(A + B\right) - \sin\left(A - B\right)\right].$ (1)

$$\sum_{k=1}^{n}\sin\left(\tfrac{1}{2}x\right)\cos\left(kx\right)$$

$$= \sin\left(\tfrac{1}{2}x\right)\cos\left(x\right) + \sin\left(\tfrac{1}{2}x\right)\cos\left(2x\right) + \sin\left(\tfrac{1}{2}x\right)\cos\left(3x\right) + \cdots + \sin\left(\tfrac{1}{2}x\right)\cos\left(nx\right)$$

$$\frac{1}{2}\left[\sin\left(\tfrac{3}{2}x\right) - \sin\left(\tfrac{1}{2}x\right)\right] + \frac{1}{2}\left[\sin\left(\tfrac{5}{2}x\right) - \sin\left(\tfrac{3}{2}x\right)\right] + \frac{1}{2}\left[\sin\left(\tfrac{7}{2}x\right) - \sin\left(\tfrac{5}{2}x\right)\right] +$$

$$\cdots + \frac{1}{2}\left[\sin\left(\tfrac{2n+1}{2}x\right)\right] - \sin\left(\tfrac{2n-1}{2}x\right)$$

$$= \frac{1}{2}\left[\sin\left(\tfrac{2n+1}{2}x\right) - \sin\left(\tfrac{1}{2}x\right)\right]$$

The right side of the identity equals $\sin\left(\tfrac{n}{2}x\right)\cos\left(\tfrac{n+1}{2}x\right)$

$$= \frac{1}{2}\left[\sin\left(\tfrac{2n+1}{2}x\right) - \sin\left(\tfrac{1}{2}x\right)\right] \quad \text{(using formula (1))}$$

Hence, $\displaystyle\sum_{k=1}^{n}\sin\left(\tfrac{1}{2}x\right)\cos\left(kx\right) = \sin\left(\tfrac{n}{2}x\right)\cos\left(\tfrac{n+1}{2}x\right)$.

Calculus - II

1. Solution

    (a) $\lim\limits_{x \to 2} \dfrac{x^2 - 4}{x - 2} = \lim\limits_{x \to 2} \dfrac{(x-2)(x+2)}{(x-2)}$

    $= \lim\limits_{x \to 2} (x + 2)$

    $= 4$

    (b) The slope of the tangent is given by the value of $\dfrac{dy}{dx}$ at $x = -\pi$.

    $\dfrac{dy}{dx} = (1)(\sin x) + (x)(\cos x)$

    At $x = -\pi$, $\dfrac{dy}{dx} = (1)(0) + (-\pi)(-1) = \pi$.

    The slope of the tangent line is π.

    (c) $f'(x) = 2(\cos x)(-\sin x)$

    $f'\left(\dfrac{\pi}{4}\right) = 2\left(\dfrac{1}{\sqrt{2}}\right)\left(-\dfrac{1}{\sqrt{2}}\right) = -1$

    (d) $f(x) = e^x - e^{-x}$

    $f'(x) = e^x - \left(e^{-x}\right)(-1)$

    $= e^x + e^{-x}$

    $f'(0) = 1 + 1 = 2$

2. Solution

    (a) $y = \dfrac{3}{x(x + 3)}$

    Since $\lim\limits_{x \to 0^-} y = -\infty$ and $\lim\limits_{x \to 0^+} y = +\infty$, $x = 0$ is an asymptote.

    Since $\lim\limits_{x \to -3^-} y = -\infty$ and $\lim\limits_{x \to -3^+} y = +\infty$, $x = -3$ is an asymptote.

    Since $\lim\limits_{x \to \pm\infty} y = 0$, $y = 0$ is an asymptote.

    (b)

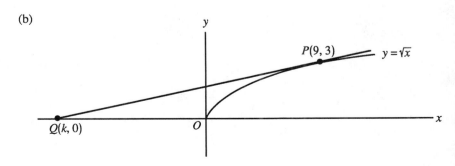

For the given curve, the slope of the tangent line at any point is given by

$$\frac{dy}{dx} = \frac{1}{2\sqrt{x}}.$$

At $P(9, 3)$, the slope of the tangent is $\frac{1}{6}$.

If Q has coordinates $(k, 0)$, then $\dfrac{1}{6} = \dfrac{3}{9 - k}$

$$k = -9$$

Hence, P and Q are equidistant from the y-axis.

Thus, the midpoint of PQ has x-coordinate 0 and is on the y-axis.

3. Solution

If $r(t) = 4t^2 + 3t + 1$, $\dfrac{dr}{dt} = 8t + 3$.

When $\dfrac{dr}{dt} = 11$, $8t + 3 = 11$ and $t = 1$.

The area of the circle at time t is $A(t) = \pi[r(t)]^2$.

Thus $\dfrac{dA}{dt} = 2\pi r(t)\dfrac{dr}{dt}$.

When $t = 1$, $\dfrac{dA}{dt} = 2\pi[r(1)](11)$

$$= (22\pi)(8)$$
$$= 176\pi$$

The rate of change of the area of the circle when $\dfrac{dr}{dt} = 11$ is 176π.

4. Solution

Let the coordinates of the vertex that lies on the parabola be $P(x, 12 - x^2)$.

The area of the rectangle is

$$A(x) = x(12 - x^2)$$
$$= 12x - x^3, \text{ where } 0 \le x \le 2\sqrt{3}.$$

The derivative of $A(x)$ is

$$A'(x) = 12 - 3x^2.$$

$A'(x) = 0$ when $x = 2$.

Since $A(0) = 0$, $A(2) = 16$, and $A(2\sqrt{3}) = 0$,

the maximum area of such a rectangle is 16.

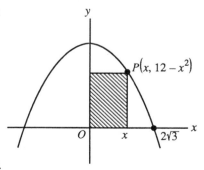

5. Solution

    Let the coordinates of any point on the first
    quadrant branch of the hyperbola be $P\left(k, \frac{3}{k}\right)$.
    The slope of the tangent to the hyperbola at
    any point is given by $\frac{dy}{dx} = -\frac{3}{x^2}$.

    At $x = k$, the slope of the tangent is $-\frac{3}{k^2}$.

    The equation of the tangent at P is

    $$y - \frac{3}{k} = -\frac{3}{k^2}(x - k).$$

    The x-intercept of this line is $2k$ and the
    y-intercept is $\frac{6}{k}$.

    The area of triangle AOB is $\frac{1}{2}(2k)\left(\frac{6}{k}\right) = 6$.

    Since the area is a constant, it is independent of
    the position of P.

    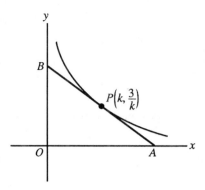

6. Solution

    Let the width of the building be x feet.
    Since the total area is 20 000 sq. ft., the length
    of the building is $\frac{20\,000}{x}$ feet.
    The cost of building the walls is

    $$C(x) = 300x + 41x + 100\left(\frac{20\,000}{x} + \frac{20\,000}{x} + x\right), \quad x > 0$$

    $$= 441x + \frac{4\,000\,000}{x}$$

    $$C'(x) = 441 - \frac{4\,000\,000}{x^2}$$

    Solving $C'(x) = 0$ gives $x = \frac{2000}{21}$.

    $$C''(x) = \frac{8\,000\,000}{x^3}$$

    Since $C''(x)$ is positive for all $x > 0$, $C(x)$ has an
    absolute minimum value when $x = \frac{2000}{21}$.
    The dimensions of the building that yield a
    minimum cost are $\frac{2000}{21}$ ft. by 210 ft.

7. Solution

Note the value of first making a sketch.
It shows that there will be only one point
satisfying the given conditions.

Let P be $\left(a, \dfrac{1}{a^2}\right)$.

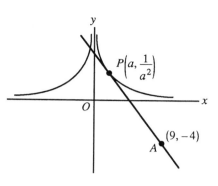

The slope of the tangent line at any point
(x, y) on the given curve is given by

$$\frac{dy}{dx} = -\frac{2}{x^3}.$$

Hence, the slope of the tangent line at P is
$-\dfrac{2}{a^3}$.

Since the tangent line passes through the point $A(9, -4)$, the slope of PA is the same
as the slope of the tangent line.

Thus,

$$\frac{\dfrac{1}{a^2} + 4}{a - 9} = -\frac{2}{a^3}$$

$$4a^3 + 3a - 18 = 0$$

$$(2a - 3)\left(2a^2 + 3a + b\right) = 0$$

One solution is $a = \dfrac{3}{2}$.

The second factor results in roots that are complex numbers.

The only point satisfying the property is $\left(\dfrac{3}{2}, \dfrac{4}{9}\right)$.

8. Solution

Let the can have radius r cm and height h cm.

Then the volume of the can is $V = \pi r^2 h = k$.   (1)

The cost, C, of the material required for the wall, top, and bottom is

$$C = 2(2\pi rh) + 2\pi r^2$$

$$= 4\pi rh + 2\pi r^2$$

From (1), $h = \dfrac{k}{\pi r^2}$.

Now $C = \dfrac{4k}{r} + 2\pi r^2$.

Since r is the radius of the can, $r \geq 0$.

As r approaches 0 through positive values, C becomes large without limit.

Also as r increases without bound, C increases in like fashion.

Hence the minimal value for C occurs for the value of r which makes the derivative 0.

Setting $\dfrac{dC}{dr} = 0$ we obtain $-\dfrac{4k}{r^2} + 4\pi r = 0$ or $r^3 = \dfrac{k}{\pi}$.

Using (1), this is equivalent to $r^3 = \frac{\pi r^2 h}{\pi} = r^2 h$ and so $r = h$.

The ratio of the height to the radius is $1:1$.

9. Solution

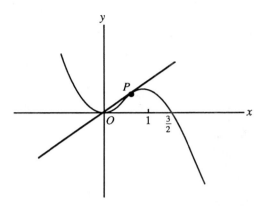

The graph illustrates the geometric nature of the problem. We can see that there is only one point other than the origin which satisfies the given conditions.

Let the point be $P(a, 3a^2 - 2a^3)$.

The slope of the tangent line to the given curve at any point is given by $\frac{dy}{dx} = 6x - 6x^2$.

The slope of the tangent line at P is $6a - 6a^2$.

Since this tangent line goes through the origin, its slope is also given by

$$\frac{3a^2 - 2a^3 - 0}{a - 0} = 3a - 2a^2, \; a \neq 0.$$

Thus, $6a - 6a^2 = 3a - 2a^2$

$$4a^2 - 3a = 0$$

$$a(4a - 3) = 0$$

Since $a \neq 0$, $a = \frac{3}{4}$.

Hence, P is $\left(\frac{3}{4}, \frac{27}{32}\right)$.

10. Solution

Let the given number be x.

The expression to be considered is $f(x) = x + \frac{1}{x} + \frac{3}{x^2}, \; x > 0$.

To show that $f(x) \geq \frac{13}{4}$ we must find the minimum value of $f(x)$.

Consider $f'(x) = 1 - \frac{1}{x^2} - \frac{6}{x^3}$

$$= \frac{x^3 - x - 6}{x^3}$$

Since $x > 0$, the only critical values of f occurs when

$$x^3 - x - 6 = 0 \qquad (1)$$
$$(x - 2)(x^2 + 2x + 3) = 0$$

The only real solution of (1) is $x = 2$.

x	$0 < x < 2$	2	$x > 2$
$f'(x)$	–	0	$+$
$f(x)$	decreasing	local minimum	increasing

Thus, $f(2) = 2 + \frac{1}{2} + \frac{3}{4} = \frac{13}{4}$ is the minimum value of $f(x)$.

Hence, the value of the given expression is never less than $\frac{13}{4}$.

11. Solution

Let the dimensions of the box be as shown in the diagram.

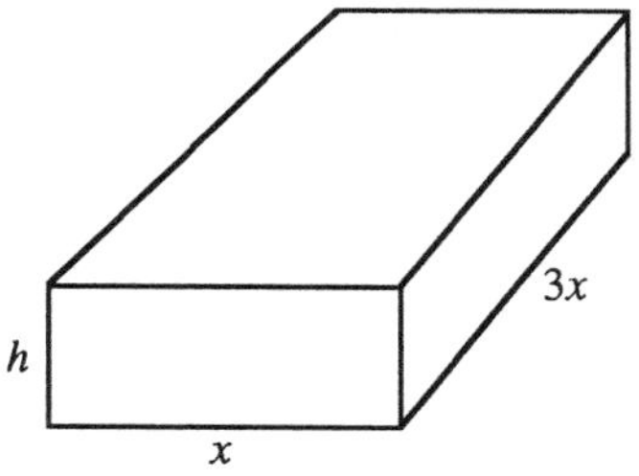

The volume V of the box is

$$V = (h)(x)(3x)$$
$$= 3x^2h \qquad (1)$$

We are given that the surface area is 30 square feet.

Hence, $2(hx + 3x^2 + 3xh) = 30$ and

$$h = \frac{15 - 3x^2}{4x}.$$

In order that all dimensions be positive, the restrictions on x are $0 < x < \sqrt{5}$.

Substituting for h in (1) gives

$$V = 3x^2\left(\frac{15 - 3x^2}{4x}\right)$$
$$= \frac{9}{4}(5x - x^3)$$
$$\frac{dV}{dx} = \frac{9}{4}(5 - 3x^2)$$

Solving $\frac{dV}{dx} = 0$ yields

$$5 - 3x^2 = 0$$
$$x = \sqrt{\frac{5}{3}}$$

As $x \to 0^+$, $V \to 0$.

As $x \to \sqrt{5}$, $V \to 0$.

At $x = \sqrt{\frac{5}{3}}$, $V = \frac{5}{2}\sqrt{15}$.

The volume of the box is a maximum when the dimensions are $\sqrt{\frac{5}{3}} \times \sqrt{15} \times \sqrt{\frac{15}{2}}$.

12. Solution

(a) $f(x) = 1 - \frac{2}{x}$ and $f'(x) = \frac{2}{x^2}$.

$$g'(x) = \frac{(x^2 - 5x)(1) - (x + 3)(2x - 5)}{(x^2 - 5x)^2}.$$

Hence, $f'(1) = 2$ and $g'(1) = \frac{(-4)(1) - (4)(-3)}{(4)^2} = \frac{1}{2}$.

Since $f'(1)\, g'(1) \neq -1$, we conclude that the curves are not orthogonal at $(1, -1)$.

(b) To find the points of intersection of f and g we solve the equation

$$\frac{x - 2}{x} = \frac{x + 3}{x^2 - 5x}$$
$$x(x - 5)(x - 2) = x(x + 3)$$
$$x(x^2 - 8x + 7) = 0$$
$$x(x - 1)(x - 7) = 0$$

Now $x \neq 0$, since neither curve is defined for $x = 0$.

The other point of intersection is $\left(7, \frac{5}{7}\right)$.

(c) At $x = 7, f'(7) = \frac{2}{49}$.

The equation of required tangent line is $y - \frac{5}{7} = \frac{2}{49}(x - 7)$.

13. Solution

(a) By observation, there are three inflection points. Of these, one has its x-value to the left of -2, one has its x-value between -2 and 0, and the third has its x-value between 0 and 3.

(b) By observation, there are three solutions to the equation $f(x) = -4$, with one in each of the intervals given in part (a).

(c) Since $\lim\limits_{x \to 3^+} \frac{1}{f(x)} = +\infty$ and $\lim\limits_{x \to 3^-} \frac{1}{f(x)} = -\infty$, then $x = 3$ is a vertical asymptote to the graph of $y = g(x)$.

Also, $\lim\limits_{x \to +\infty} \frac{1}{f(x)} = 0$ and $\lim\limits_{x \to -\infty} \frac{1}{f(x)} = 0$.

Hence, $y = 0$ is a horizontal asymptote to the graph of $y = g(x)$.

There are no other asymptotes to $y = g(x)$.

(d) From the graph we observe that

    (i)   if $x \le -2$, then $|f(x)| \le |x|$ since the graph of $y = f(x)$ is closer to the x-axis than the graph of $y = x$.

          Hence, $[f(x)]^2 \le x^2$.

    (ii)   if $-2 < x < 2$, then $|f(x)| > |x|$.

          Hence, $[f(x)]^2 > x^2$.

    (iii) if $x \ge 2$, then $f(x) \le x$.

          Hence, $[f(x)]^2 \le x^2$.

Thus, $[f(x)]^2 \le x^2$ for $x \le -2$ or $x \ge 2$.

14. Solution

The graph of $y = f(x) = x$ is a straight line through the origin having slope 1. It has no local extreme points.

The graph of $y = g(x)$ can be derived by summing the y-coordinates of the straight line $y = x$ and the hyperbola $y = \dfrac{4}{x - 2}$ which has a vertical asymptote $x = 2$ and a horizontal asymptote $y = 0$.

This process is illustrated in the accompanying diagram.

Thus, the graph of $y = g(x)$ has asymptotes $x = 2$ and $y = x$.

This can be verified by evaluating the limits:

$$\lim_{x \to +\infty} \; [x - g(x)] = 0$$

$$\lim_{x \to -\infty} \; [x - g(x)] = 0$$

$$\lim_{x \to 2^-} \; g(x) = -\infty$$

$$\lim_{x \to 2^+} \; g(x) = +\infty$$

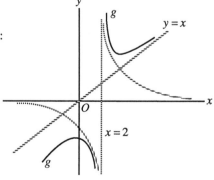

For a more detailed analysis of $y = g(x)$ we
investigate $g'(x)$ and $g''(x)$.

$$g'(x) = 1 - \frac{4}{(x-2)^2}$$

For extrema we solve $g'(x) = 0$.

$$(x-2)^2 = 4$$
$$x = 0 \ \text{ or } \ x = 4$$

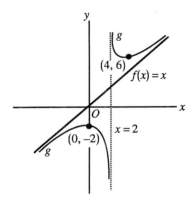

	$x < 0$	$x = 0$	$0 < x < 4$	$x = 4$	$x > 4$
$g'(x)$	+	0	−	0	+
$g(x)$	increasing	local max.	decreasing	local min.	increasing

There is a local maximum at $(0, -2)$ and a local minimum at $(4, 6)$.

Since $g''(x) = \dfrac{8}{(x-2)^3}$, we observe that the graph of $y = g(x)$ is concave down for $x < 2$
and concave up for $x > 2$.

There are no points of inflection.

Since there are no values of x that satisfy $f(x) = g(x)$, the graphs do not intersect.

15. <u>Solution</u>
    Preliminary Sketch

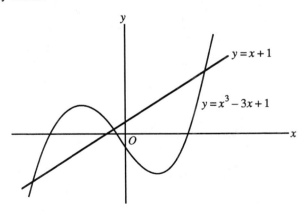

(a) The graph of $y = x + 1$ is a straight line and as such has no minima or maxima.

For $y = x^3 - 3x + 1$, the graph has local extrema when $\dfrac{dy}{dx} = 0$.

$\dfrac{dy}{dx} = 3x^2 - 3 = 0$ for $x = \pm 1$.

$\dfrac{d^2y}{dx^2} = 6x$

x	$x = -1$	$-1 < x < 0$	$x = 0$	$0 < x < 1$	$x = 1$
$f'(x)$	0				0
$f''(x)$	$-$	$-$	0	$+$	$+$
$f(x)$	local maximum	concave down	point of inflection	concave up	local minimum

Thus, $(-1, 3)$ is a local maximum, $(1, -1)$ is a local minimum and $(0, 1)$ is a point of inflection.

To find the points of intersection of the line and the cubic polynomial, we solve the equation

$$x^3 - 3x + 1 = x + 1$$
$$x^3 - 4x = 0$$
$$x(x - 2)(x + 2) = 0$$

The points of intersection are $(-2, -1)$, $(0, 1)$, and $(2, 3)$.

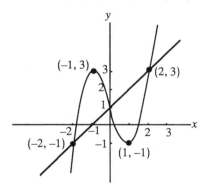

(b) The solution of the inequality $x + 1 > x^3 - 3x + 1$ is the set of all x for which the graph of the line is above that of the cubic polynomial.

The solution is $x < -2$ or $0 < x < 2$.

16. Solution

A sketch is drawn to illustrate the information given in the problem.

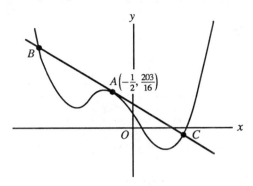

The slope of the tangent line at any point on the graph is given by

$$\frac{dy}{dx} = 12x^3 + 24x^2 - 12x - 24$$

The slope of the tangent line at A is $-\frac{12}{8} + \frac{24}{4} + \frac{12}{2} - 24 = -\frac{27}{2}$.

The equation of the tangent line at A is

$$y - \frac{203}{16} = -\frac{27}{2}\left(x + \frac{1}{2}\right)$$

or $\qquad y = -\frac{27}{2}x + \frac{95}{16}$ $\qquad\qquad\qquad$ (1)

We now solve (1) with the given curve to find the points of intersection.

$$\frac{-27}{2}x + \frac{95}{16} = 3x^4 + 8x^3 - 6x^2 - 24x + 3$$

$$48x^4 + 128x^3 - 96x^2 - 168x - 47 = 0 \qquad (2)$$

Since A is a point of tangency, $x = -\frac{1}{2}$ is a double root of (2).

Thus $48x^4 + 128x^3 - 96x^2 - 168x - 47 = (2x + 1)^2(ax^2 + bx + c)$.

By comparison of coefficients, it follows that $a = 12$, $b = 20$, and $c = -47$.

The solution of the quadratic equation $12x^2 + 20x - 47 = 0$ will yield the x-coordinates of B and C.

17. Solution

At time t, P is $2t$ units from A, so PC is $60 - 2t$.

Let the distance from the midpoint of BC to Q be x. Note that $0 \le t < 30$ and $0 \le x < 30$.

We are given that $\triangle PQC = \frac{1}{2}\triangle ABC$

$$\frac{1}{2}(PC)(QC)\sin 60° = \frac{1}{2} \cdot \frac{1}{2}(BC)(AC)\sin 60°$$

$$\frac{1}{2}(60 - 2t)(30 + x) = \frac{1}{4}(60)^2$$

$$(30 - t)(30 + x) = 900$$

Hence, $x = \dfrac{30t}{30 - t}$.

The rate of change of Q's position at any time t is given by

$$\frac{dx}{dt} = \frac{(30 - t)30 - 30t(-1)}{(30 - t)^2} = \frac{900}{(30 - t)^2}$$

For Q's rate to be the same as that of P,

$$\frac{dx}{dt} = 2$$

$$\frac{900}{(30 - t)^2} = 2$$

$$(30 - t)^2 = 450$$

$$30 - t = \pm 15\sqrt{2}$$

$$t = 30 \pm 15\sqrt{2}$$

But since $0 \le t \le 30$, $t = 30 + 15\sqrt{2}$ is not admissible.

The time at which Q's rate is equal to P's rate is $(30 - 15\sqrt{2})$ seconds.

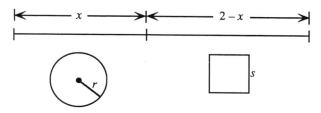

18. <u>Solution</u>

Let the portions of the wire used to form the circle and the square have lengths x m and $(2 - x)$ m respectively.

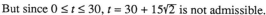

Circumference:	$x = 2\pi r$	Perimeter:	$2 - x = 4s$
Radius:	$r = \dfrac{x}{2\pi}$	Length of Side:	$s = \dfrac{2 - x}{4}$
Area:	$A = \pi\left(\dfrac{x}{2\pi}\right)^2$	Area:	$A = \left(\dfrac{2 - x}{4}\right)^2$

The expression which we want to minimize and maximize is

$$f(x) = \pi\left(\frac{x}{2\pi}\right)^2 + \left(\frac{2 - x}{4}\right)^2,\ 0 \le x \le 2$$

The derivative is $f'(x) = 2\pi\left(\dfrac{x}{2\pi}\right)\left(\dfrac{1}{2\pi}\right) + 2\left(\dfrac{2 - x}{4}\right)\left(-\dfrac{1}{4}\right)$

$$= \frac{x}{2\pi} + \frac{x - 2}{8}$$

For extreme values, solve $f'(x) = 0$.

$$4x + \pi x - 2\pi = 0$$

$$x = \frac{2\pi}{4 + \pi}$$

We now evaluate $f(x)$ at the values $x = 0$, $x = \frac{2\pi}{4 + \pi}$, and $x = 2$.

$$f(0) = \frac{1}{4}, \; f\left(\frac{2\pi}{4 + \pi}\right) = \frac{1}{\pi + 4}, \; f(2) = \frac{1}{\pi}$$

The total area has minimum value $\frac{1}{\pi + 4}$ when the radius is $\frac{1}{\pi + 4}$.

The total area has maximum value $\frac{1}{\pi}$ when the radius is $\frac{1}{\pi}$.

19. <u>Solution</u>

The derivative of $f(x)$ is

$$\begin{aligned}
f'(x) &= -\frac{1}{(1 + x)^2} + \frac{x + k - x}{(x + k)^2} \\
&= \frac{-(x + k)^2 + k(1 + x)^2}{(1 + x)^2 (x + k)^2} \\
&= \frac{x^2(k - 1) + k - k^2}{(1 + x)^2(x + k)^2}
\end{aligned} \qquad (1)$$

Since $x > 0$ and $k > 0$, the denominator of (1) is always greater than zero. Thus, the only extremal values occur when

$$x^2(k - 1) + k - k^2 = 0$$

$$x^2(k - 1) = k(k - 1)$$

If $k \neq 1$, $x = \sqrt{k}$ is a critical value.

We will use the second derivative test for extremal values.

$$f''(x) = \frac{2}{(1 + x)^3} - \frac{2k}{(x + k)^3}$$

$$f''(\sqrt{k}) = \frac{2}{(1 + \sqrt{k})^3} - \frac{2k}{(\sqrt{k} + k)^3} = \frac{2(k - 1)}{\sqrt{k}(1 + \sqrt{k})^3}$$

For $k < 1$, $f''(\sqrt{k}) < 0$ and $x = \sqrt{k}$ produces a maximum value of $\frac{2}{1 + \sqrt{k}}$.

For $k > 1$, $f''(\sqrt{k}) > 0$, so $x = \sqrt{k}$ produces a minimum value for $f(x)$.

Since $f(x)$ is continuous for $x > 0$ and $x = \sqrt{k}$ is the only value for which $f'(x) = 0$, there is no maximum value of $f(x)$ for $k > 1$.

If $k = 1$, $f(x) = \frac{1}{1 + x} + \frac{x}{x + 1} = 1$, a constant function.

Thus, if $k = 1$, the maximum value of $f(x)$ is 1.

We conclude that for $0 < k \leq 1$, the maximum value of $f(x)$ is $\frac{2}{1 + \sqrt{k}}$, and for $k > 1$, there is no maximum.

20. Solution

Let DB be z and note that since we are dealing with squares, $AD = BE = 1 - z$, so $CD = 1 - x - z$.

Now triangle FCD is similar to triangle DBE, so

$$\frac{x}{1 - x - z} = \frac{z}{1 - z}$$

Hence, $x(1 - z) = z(1 - x - z)$ and so $x = z - z^2$.

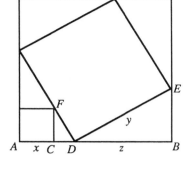

From triangle DBE, $y^2 = z^2 + (1 - z)^2$

$$= 1 - 2z + 2z^2$$
$$= 1 - 2(z - z^2)$$
$$= 1 - 2x$$

Since $x \geq 0$ and $x = z - z^2$, the range of values for x is determined by the vertex of the parabola in the diagram.

Since $\frac{dx}{dz} = 1 - 2z$, the vertex occurs where $\frac{dx}{dz} = 0$.

Solving $1 - 2z = 0$ yields $z = \frac{1}{2}$.

The vertex is the point $\left(\frac{1}{2}, \frac{1}{4}\right)$.

The range of values for x is $0 \leq x \leq \frac{1}{4}$.

The quantity $x^2 + y^2 = x^2 + (1 - 2x)$

$$= (x - 1)^2$$
$$= g(x)$$

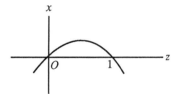

To determine the minimum value of $g(x)$ where $0 \leq x \leq \frac{1}{4}$, we solve $g'(x) = 0$

$$2(x - 1) = 0$$
$$x = 1$$

This value is not in the domain of $g(x)$.

The minimum value of $g(x)$ must occur at $x = 0$ or $x = \frac{1}{4}$.

Since $g(0) = 1$ and $g\left(\frac{1}{4}\right) = \frac{9}{16}$, the minimum value of $x^2 + y^2$ is $\frac{9}{16}$ and occurs when $x = \frac{1}{4}$ and $y = \frac{1}{\sqrt{2}}$.

21. Solution

From the definition of derivative,

$$f'(x) = \lim_{h \to 0} \frac{f(x + h) - f(x)}{h}$$

$$= \lim_{h \to 0} \frac{f(x)f(h) - f(x)}{h}, \text{ using the first given property of } f$$

$$= \lim_{h \to 0} \frac{f(x)(f(h) - 1)}{h}$$

$$= \lim_{h \to 0} \frac{f(x)(1 + hg(h) - 1)}{h}, \text{ using the second given property of } f$$

$$= f(x) \lim_{h \to 0} g(h)$$

$$= f(x)(1)$$

$$= f(x)$$

Hence, $f'(x) = f(x)$ for all x.

22. Solution

By writing the given equation in the form

$$\frac{(x - t)^2}{4} + \frac{y^2}{16} = 1, t > 0,$$

we can identify the family of conics to be
ellipses, each having centre $(t, 0)$ and minor
axis of length 4.

For any point $P(x, y)$ on the given ellipse,
the square of the distance PO is given by

$$(PO)^2 = x^2 + y^2 \qquad (1)$$

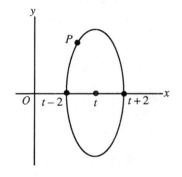

Since P is on the ellipse, its coordinates
satisfy the given equation.

Therefore $4(x - t)^2 + y^2 = 16$ (2)

Substituting for y^2 from (2) into (1) gives

$$(OP)^2 = x^2 + 16 - 4(x - t)^2 = F(x)$$

where x must lie in the interval $t - 2 \le x \le t + 2$.

To find the extreme values of $(OP)^2$, we solve
$F'(x) = 0$.

$$2x - 8(x - t) = 0$$

$$x = \frac{4}{3} t$$

We now evaluate $F(x)$ at $x = \frac{4}{3}t$, $x = t - 2$, and
$x = t + 2$.

$$F\left(\tfrac{4}{3}t\right) = \tfrac{16}{9}t^2 + 16 - 4\left(\tfrac{t^2}{9}\right) = \tfrac{4}{3}t^2 + 16$$

$$F(t-2) = (t-2)^2 + 16 - 4(-2)^2 = (t-2)^2$$

$$F(t+2) = (t+2)^2 + 16 - 4(2)^2 = (t+2)^2$$

A sketch of these three parabolas will assist with the further development of the solution.

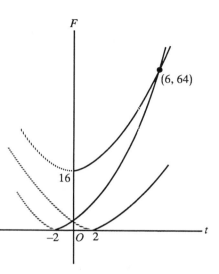

The minimum value of $(OP)^2$ is

$L(t) = (t-2)^2$ for all values of t.

The maximum value of $(OP)^2$ is

$G(t) = \tfrac{4}{3}t^2 + 16$ for $0 < t \le 6$, and is

$G(t) = (t+2)^2$ for $t > 6$.

We now must consider two cases for minimizing $L(t) + G(t)$.

If $0 < t \le 6$, $G(t) + L(t) = \tfrac{4}{3}t^2 + 16 + (t-2)^2$

$$= \tfrac{7}{3}t^2 - 4t + 20$$

For a minimum, $\tfrac{14}{3}t - 4 = 0$ and $t = \tfrac{6}{7}$.

The minimum value is $G\left(\tfrac{6}{7}\right) + L\left(\tfrac{6}{7}\right) = \tfrac{128}{7}$.

If $t > 6$, $G(t) + L(t) = (t+2)^2 + (t-2)^2$

$$= 2t^2 + 8$$

$$> 80$$

Hence, $t = \tfrac{6}{7}$ minimizes $G(t) + L(t)$.

Euclidean Geometry: Polygons

1. Solution
   Since AB, BC, and CA are all diagonals of the faces of the cube, their lengths are equal.
   Therefore, $\triangle ABC$ is equilateral and so the acute angle between AB and BC is 60°.

2. Solution
   The altitude AD of isosceles $\triangle ABC$ meets base BC at its midpoint and so $BD = DC = 6$.

   The area of $\triangle ABC = \frac{1}{2}(BC)(AD) = 48$

   $$\frac{1}{2}(12)AD = 48$$

   $$AD = 8$$

   Now, in $\triangle ABD$, $(AB)^2 = 6^2 + 8^2$ [Pythagorean
   $\qquad\qquad\qquad = 100$ Theorem]
   Therefore, $\qquad AB = 10$.

   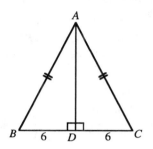

3. Solution
   By the Pythagorean Theorem,
   $$CB = \sqrt{17^2 - 8^2}$$
   $$= \sqrt{225}$$
   $$= 15$$
   Since $CD = DB = \frac{1}{2}CB$, then $DB = \frac{15}{2}$.
   The area of $\triangle ADB = \frac{1}{2}(DB)(AC)$
   $$= \frac{1}{2}\left(\frac{15}{2}\right)(8)$$
   $$= 30$$

   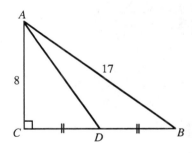

4. Solution
   A cube has 12 edges. To keep the maximum number of edges, a triangle is formed at each of the 8 corners of the cube, while still retaining a part of each edge of the original cube.
   So the number of edges of the resulting solid is
   $12 + (8 \times 3) = 36$.

   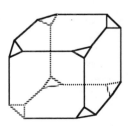

5. Solution

    Since $\angle ABC = \angle ADE$, and $\angle A$ is common,

    $\triangle ABC$ is similar to $\triangle ADE$.

    Therefore, $\dfrac{AB}{AD} = \dfrac{AC}{AE}$

    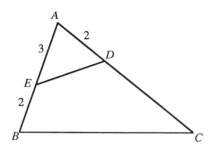

    $$\frac{5}{2} = \frac{DC + 2}{3}$$

    $$2(DC + 2) = 15$$

    $$DC + 2 = \frac{15}{2}$$

    $$DC = 5.5$$

6. Solution

    If the area of $\triangle LMP$ is 20 cm², and the base
    is 5 cm, then the altitude from P to a line
    through L and M must be 8 cm long.
    The set of points, P, 8 cm from LM, is a
    pair of lines parallel to LM, as shown in the
    diagram.

    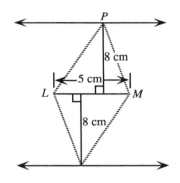

7. Solution

    Let $PA = PD = PR = x$.

    Construct $PQ \perp AD$.

    Then $PQ = 16 - x$.

    In $\triangle PAQ$, by the Pythagorean Theorem,

    $$x^2 = 8^2 + (16 - x)^2$$

    $$x^2 = 64 + 256 - 32x + x^2$$

    $$32x = 320$$

    $$x = 10$$

    The required distance is 10.

    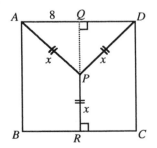

8. Solution

    The area of a triangle is $\frac{1}{2}$(base)(height).

    Here, the base is 4.

    For a maximum area, we require the height
    to be a maximum, which will occur when
    $\angle ABC = 90°$.

    Hence, the maximum area is $\frac{1}{2}(4)(4) = 8$.

    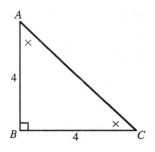

9. Solution 1

    In the diagram, AB, BC, and CD are three
    sides of the decagon.

    AB and DC extended meet at E.

    $\angle BEC$ is one of the ten angles at the points
    of the star.

    The sum of the exterior angles of any
    polygon is 360°.

    Since the decagon is regular, $\angle EBC = \angle ECB$

    $$= \frac{360°}{10}$$
    $$= 36°$$

    Hence, $\angle BEC = 180° - 2(36°) = 108°$.

    Since there are 10 points to the star, the sum of the angles at the points is
    $10(108°) = 1080°$.

    Solution 2

    Construct the diagram, as in Solution 1.

    The sum of the interior angles of a decagon is

    $(n-2)180° = (10-2)180°$
    $$= 1440°$$

    Since the decagon is regular, $\angle ABC = \angle BCD$

    $$= \frac{1440°}{10}$$
    $$= 144°$$

    Now, $\angle EBC = \angle ECB = 180° - 144° = 36°$.

    Hence, $\angle BEC = 180° - 2(36°) = 108°$.

    Since there are 10 points to the star, the sum of the angles at the points is
    $10(108°) = 1080°$.

10. <u>Solution</u>

In the diagram, the shaded region indicates the volume of the water when the aquarium is tipped.

The volume of the water is

$$V = (\text{area of base}) \times (\text{height})$$
$$= \left(\tfrac{1}{2} \times 24 \times 15\right) \times 20$$

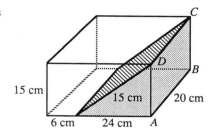

If d cm is the depth of the water when the aquarium is level,

$$d \times 30 \times 20 = \tfrac{1}{2} \times 24 \times 15 \times 20$$
$$d = 6$$

11. <u>Solution</u>

Since $DK{:}KC = 3{:}2$, then $DC{:}KC = 5{:}2$.

The areas of similar figures are proportional to the squares of the lengths of their corresponding sides.

Thus, $\dfrac{\text{rectangle } ABCD}{\text{rectangle } EFGH} = \dfrac{(DC)^2}{(KC)^2} = \dfrac{25}{4}$.

12. <u>Solution</u>

In the diagram, ABC represents the right-angled triangle formed by drawing the perpendicular from the centre of the ball to meet the diagonal of the bottom face at its midpoint. Then the required distance from the ball to the vertex is BC.

The diagonal of each face of the cube is

$\sqrt{14^2 + 14^2} = 14\sqrt{2}$, and so $AC = 7\sqrt{2}$.

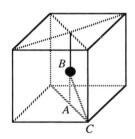

Therefore, $BC = \sqrt{(AB)^2 + (AC)^2}$
$$= \sqrt{36 + 98}$$
$$= \sqrt{134}$$

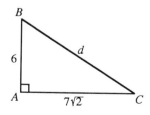

13. Solution

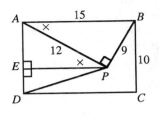

Since $(AB)^2 = (AP)^2 + (PB)^2$, $\angle APB = 90°$.

Join PD and draw $PE \perp AD$.

Since AB is parallel to EP, $\angle APE = \angle PAB$.

Thus, $\triangle ABP$ is similar to $\triangle PAE$.

Hence, $\dfrac{15}{12} = \dfrac{9}{AE} = \dfrac{12}{EP}$.

This yields $AE = \frac{36}{5}$, $EP = \frac{48}{5}$ and

$ED = 10 - \frac{36}{5} = \frac{14}{5}$.

In triangle PED, $(PD)^2 = \left(\frac{14}{5}\right)^2 + \left(\frac{48}{5}\right)^2$, and so

$PD = 10$.

14. Solution

The shaded area is given by $(AC)^2 - (AB)^2 = 31$.

Therefore, $(AC - AB)(AC + AB) = 31$.

Since AB and AC are positive integers, then $AC - AB = 1$ (1)

and $AC + AB = 31$. (2)

Solving (1) and (2) gives $AC = 16$ and $AB = 15$.

Therefore, $BC = 1$ and, since $BC = CD$, then $CD = 1$ and $AD = 17$.

Therefore, the area of the largest square is $17^2 = 289$.

15. Solution

Each square has sides of length 4.

The total area of $ABHFGD$

= area $ABCD$ + area $DEFG$ − area $DEHC$.

Now area $\triangle DCH$ = area $\triangle DEH$

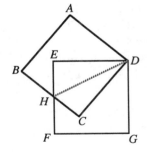

$$= \tfrac{1}{2}(DC)(CH)$$

$$= \tfrac{1}{2}(4)(2)$$

$$= 4$$

Therefore, the area of quadrilateral $DEHC = 2(4)$

$$= 8$$

Therefore, the total area of $ABHFGD$ is $4^2 + 4^2 - 8$

$$= 16 + 16 - 8$$

$$= 24$$

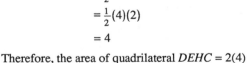

16. Solution

Let $DS = x$ cm.

Since P, Q, R, and S are coplanar, they must form a parallelogram.

Hence, slope PQ = slope SR.

Hence, $\dfrac{56-33}{11} = \dfrac{47-x}{11}$

$x = 24$

The length of DS is 24 cm.

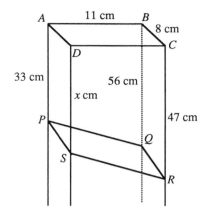

17. Solution

Let r be the radius of a dime.

The area of the shaded region is twice the area of equilateral triangle PQS.

Since the sides of a 30°-60°-90° triangle are in the ratio 1:$\sqrt{3}$:2 and $OQ = r$, then $OP = \sqrt{3}r$, and $PQ = 2r$.

Hence, the area of $\triangle PQS = \frac{1}{2}(2r)(\sqrt{3}r)$

$= \sqrt{3}\,r^2$

Therefore, the packing density is $\dfrac{2\sqrt{3}\,r^2}{4(\pi r^2)} = \dfrac{\sqrt{3}}{2\pi}$.

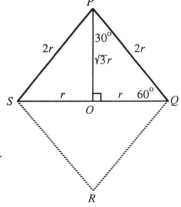

18. Solution 1

In the diagram, segment AB subtends equal angles at D and E.

Hence, the points A, B, D, and E are concyclic (actually, the circle on AB as diameter passes through D and E).

The exterior angle CDE of the cyclic quadrilateral $ABDE$ is equal to the opposite angle CAB.

Similarly, $\angle CED = \angle CBA$.

Since their three angles are equal, triangles CDE and CAB are similar.

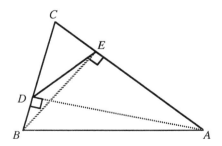

Solution 2

$\triangle CBE$ is similar to $\triangle CAD$ since $\angle C$ is common and $\angle CEB = \angle CDA = 90°$.

Therefore, $\dfrac{CB}{CA} = \dfrac{CE}{CD}$.

In $\triangle CED$ and $\triangle CAB$, $\dfrac{CB}{CA} = \dfrac{CE}{CD}$, and the contained $\angle C$ is common.

Hence, $\triangle CAB$ is similar to $\triangle CDE$.

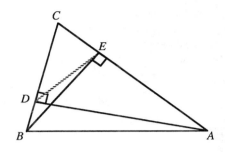

19. Solution

Since the midpoint of the hypotenuse of a right-angled triangle is equidistant from its vertices, then $BF = FA = FC$.

Therefore, $\triangle AFC$ is isosceles, and so $\angle FAC = \angle FCA$.

Also, $\angle BAD + \angle ABD = 90°$
$$= \angle ABC + \angle ACB.$$

Therefore, $\angle BAD = \angle ACB = \angle FAC$.

Now, $\angle DAE = \angle BAE - \angle BAD$
$$= \angle CAE - \angle FAC$$
$$= \angle EAF$$

Therefore, AE bisects $\angle DAF$.

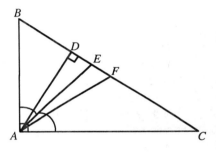

20. Solution

Let BD and CE intersect at point X.

Since the sum of the angles of a triangle is 180°, then $\angle ABC = \angle ACB = 80°$.

Therefore, $\angle EBD = 30°$, $\angle ECD = 40°$, and $\angle BDC = 50°$.

Also, all four angles at X are right angles.

Hence, $\triangle BXC \equiv \triangle CXD$.

Thus, $BX = XD$, and so $\triangle BEX \equiv \triangle DEX$.

Thus, $\angle EDX = \angle EBX = 30°$.

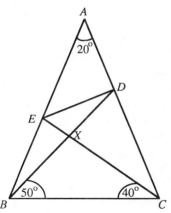

21. Solution 1

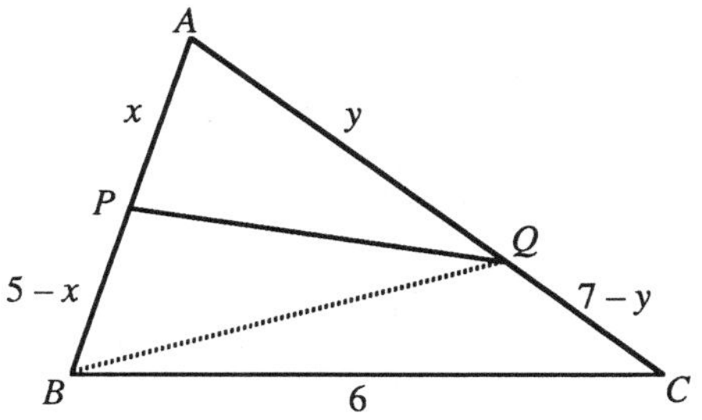

Let $AP = x$ and $AQ = y$.

Therefore, $PB = 5 - x$ and $QC = 7 - y$.

Also $PA + AQ = \frac{1}{2}$(perimeter of

$\triangle ABC$), and so $x + y = 9$.

Join BQ. Since the areas of triangles with equal heights are proportional to their bases,

$$\frac{\triangle APQ}{\triangle ABQ} = \frac{x}{5}$$

and $\dfrac{\triangle ABQ}{\triangle ABC} = \dfrac{y}{7}$

Hence, $\dfrac{\triangle APQ}{\triangle ABQ} \cdot \dfrac{\triangle ABQ}{\triangle ABC} = \dfrac{xy}{35}$ or $\dfrac{\triangle APQ}{\triangle ABC} = \dfrac{xy}{35}$.

But $\triangle APQ = \frac{1}{2} \triangle ABC$, and so

$$\frac{\frac{1}{2}\triangle ABC}{\triangle ABC} = \frac{xy}{35}$$

$$2xy = 35$$

Since $x + y = 9$,

$$2x(9 - x) = 35$$

$$2x^2 - 18x + 35 = 0$$

$$x = \frac{18 \pm \sqrt{44}}{4} = \frac{9 \pm \sqrt{11}}{2}$$

But $\dfrac{9 + \sqrt{11}}{2} > 6$, so $PB = 5 - x$ would be negative, and so $x = \dfrac{9 - \sqrt{11}}{2}$.

Therefore, $PB = 5 - x$

$$= 5 - \frac{9 - \sqrt{11}}{2}$$

$$= \frac{1 + \sqrt{11}}{2}$$

$$\approx 2.2$$

Therefore, the length of PB is 2.2, correct to one decimal place.

Solution 2

Let x be the length of PB.

Then $AP = 5 - x$.

The perimeter of $\triangle ABC$ is 18 and so $PA + AQ = 9$.

$$AQ = 9 - (5 - x)$$
$$= 4 + x$$

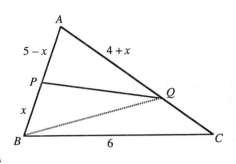

The area of $\triangle ABC$ is $\frac{1}{2}(AB)(AC) \sin A$

$$= \frac{1}{2}(5)(7) \sin A$$

and the area of $\triangle APQ$ is $\frac{1}{2}(AP)(AQ) \sin A$

$$= \frac{1}{2}(5 - x)(4 + x) \sin A$$

Since area $\triangle APQ = \frac{1}{2}$ area $\triangle ABC$,

$$\frac{1}{2}(5 - x)(4 + x) \sin A = \frac{1}{2}\left[\frac{1}{2}(5)(7) \sin A\right]$$
$$(5 - x)(4 + x) = \frac{35}{2}$$
$$2x^2 - 2x - 5 = 0$$
$$x = \frac{2 \pm \sqrt{4 + 40}}{2} = \frac{1 \pm \sqrt{11}}{2}$$

But $\dfrac{1 - \sqrt{11}}{2} < 0$ and so $x = \dfrac{1 + \sqrt{11}}{2} \approx 2.2$.

Therefore, the length of PB is 2.2, correct to one decimal place.

Solution 3

Let $AP = x$ and $AQ = y$.

Therefore, $PB = 5 - x$ and $QC = 7 - y$.

Also $PA + AQ = \frac{1}{2}$ (perimeter of $\triangle ABC$), and so $x + y = 9$.

Using Heron's formula, the area of $\triangle ABC$ is

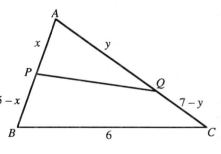

$$\sqrt{9(9 - 5)(9 - 6)(9 - 7)}$$
$$= \sqrt{9 \cdot 4 \cdot 3 \cdot 2}$$
$$= 6\sqrt{6}$$

Hence the area of $\triangle APQ = \frac{1}{2} xy \sin A = 3\sqrt{6}$

and so $xy = \dfrac{6\sqrt{6}}{\sin A}$.

Now, by the Cosine Law,

$$6^2 = 5^2 + 7^2 - 2(5)(7) \cos A,$$

from which $\cos A = \frac{19}{35}$ and hence $\sin A = \frac{12\sqrt{6}}{35}$.

Therefore, $xy = \dfrac{\frac{6\sqrt{6}}{12\sqrt{6}}}{35} = \dfrac{35}{2}$.

Now solve $x + y = 9$ and $xy = \dfrac{35}{2}$ as in Solution 1.

22. <u>Solution</u>

Let $BE = EA = x$, and let $AD = DC = y$.

In $\triangle BAD$, $4x^2 + y^2 = 25$.   (1)

In $\triangle EAC$, $x^2 + 4y^2 = 40$.   (2)

(1) + (2) gives $5x^2 + 5y^2 = 65$

$$x^2 + y^2 = 13$$

In $\triangle BAC$, $4x^2 + 4y^2 = (BC)^2$.

Therefore, $(BC)^2 = 4(x^2 + y^2)$

$$= 4(13)$$
$$= 52$$

and so $BC = \sqrt{52} = 2\sqrt{13}$.

The length of the longest side is $2\sqrt{13}$.

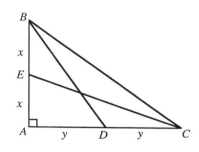

23. <u>Solution</u>

Let T be the point of intersection of DR and CS. By symmetry, the area common to the two parallelograms is four times the area of quadrilateral $ORTS$.

In triangle ODC, since S and R are the midpoints of OD and OC,

$SR \parallel DC$ and $SR = \frac{1}{2}DC = 6$ cm.

Since T is the centroid of $\triangle ODC$, $OT = 4$ cm.

The area of quadrilateral $OSTR$

$$= 2 \times \text{area of } \triangle OST$$
$$= 2 \times \left[\frac{1}{2}(4)(3)\right]$$
$$= 12 \text{ cm}^2$$

Thus, the area common to the two

parallelograms is 48 cm^2.

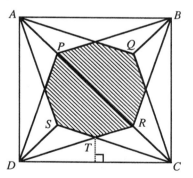

24. <u>Solution 1</u>

    Let $\angle B = x$.

    Therefore, $\angle ADC = 2x$.

    Construct DE, the bisector of $\angle ADC$ to meet AB at E.

    Therefore, $\angle ADE = \angle EDC = \angle B = x$.

    Since $DC \| AB$, $\angle AED = \angle CDE = x$
        (alternate angles).

    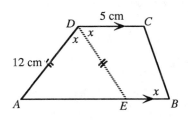

    Since $\angle ADE = \angle AED = x$, $\triangle ADE$ is isosceles.

    Therefore, $AD = AE = 12$ cm.

    Since $\angle AED = \angle B = x$,
        $DE \| CB$ (corresponding angles are equal).

    Therefore, $DEBC$ is a parallelogram.

    Hence, $EB = DC = 5$ cm.

    Therefore, $AB = AE + EB = 12 + 5 = 17$ cm.

    <u>Solution 2</u>

    Extend AD and BC to meet at E.

    Let $\angle B = x$.

    Therefore, $\angle ADC = 2x$.

    Since $DC \| AB$, $\angle A = 180° - 2x$
        (co-interior angles are supplementary).

    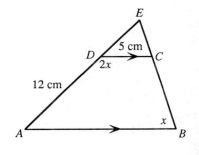

    Also, $\angle EDC = 180° - 2x$ and $\angle DCE = x$.

    Hence, $\angle E = 180° - (180° - 2x + x)$

        or $\angle E = x$.

    Since $\angle E = \angle DCE$, $\triangle DEC$ is isosceles and so $DE = 5$ cm.

    Hence, $AE = AD + DE$

    $\qquad = 12 + 5$

    $\qquad = 17$ cm

    Since $\angle E = \angle B$, then $\triangle ABE$ is isosceles and
        so $AB = AE = 17$ cm.

25. <u>Solution 1</u>

Join BE, and let areas be as follows:

$\triangle AFE = z$, $\triangle BEF = y$, $\triangle BED = \triangle DEC = x$

[$\triangle BED = \triangle DEC$ since they have equal
bases and altitudes].

Then $\triangle AEC = y + z$ [since
$\triangle ABD = \triangle ADC$].

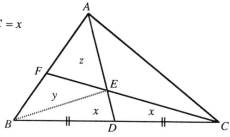

Now $\dfrac{AF}{FB} = \dfrac{\triangle AFE}{\triangle BEF}$

$\quad = \dfrac{z}{y}$

$\quad = \dfrac{\triangle AFC}{\triangle CBF}$

$\quad = \dfrac{2z + y}{2x + y}$

Thus, $\dfrac{z}{y} = \dfrac{2z + y}{2x + y}$; that is, $y^2 + yz = 2xz$.

Therefore $y(y + z) = 2xz$ and so $\dfrac{2z}{y} = \dfrac{y + z}{x}$.

Therefore, $\dfrac{2AF}{FB} = \dfrac{2z}{y} = \dfrac{y + z}{x} = \dfrac{\triangle AEC}{\triangle DEC} = \dfrac{AE}{ED}$.

<u>Solution 2</u>

Draw DG parallel to AB.

Then $\angle AFE = \angle EGD$ (alternate angles).

Also, $\angle FEA = \angle DEG$.

Then, $\triangle DEG$ is similar to $\triangle AEF$.

Hence, $\dfrac{AE}{ED} = \dfrac{AF}{DG} = \dfrac{AF}{\frac{1}{2}BF} = \dfrac{2AF}{BF}$.

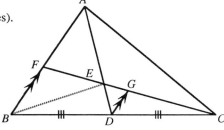

Analytic Geometry: Lines and Polygons

1. <u>Solution</u>

There are three parallelograms possible.
The area is the same for all three and is just
double the area of $\triangle ABC$.

Area $\triangle ABC = \frac{1}{2}$ (base)(height)

$\qquad = \frac{1}{2}(2)(1)$

$\qquad = 1$

The area of the parallelogram is 2.

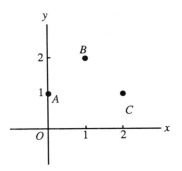

2. <u>Solution</u>

The slope of the line $2x + y = 0$ is -2.

Since the lines are perpendicular, the slope of the new line is $\frac{1}{2}$.

Since the new line passes through $(0, 0)$, its equation is $y = \frac{1}{2}x$ or $x - 2y = 0$.

3. <u>Solution 1</u>

$\text{slope } AB = \dfrac{-4 - 1}{9 - 3} = -\dfrac{5}{6}$

$\text{slope } AC = \dfrac{t - 1}{-3 - 3} = \dfrac{t - 1}{-6}$

Since A, B, and C are collinear,

$\quad$ slope AC = slope AB.

$\qquad \dfrac{t - 1}{-6} = \dfrac{5}{-6}$

$\qquad t - 1 = 5$

$\qquad\quad t = 6$

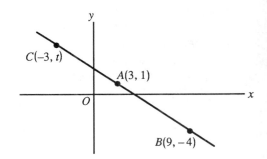

<u>Solution 2</u>

The equation of the line that passes through points A and B is $\dfrac{y - 1}{x - 3} = -\dfrac{5}{6}$.

Since $C(-3, t)$ is on the line,

$\qquad \dfrac{t - 1}{-3 - 3} = \dfrac{5}{-6}$

$\qquad\quad t - 1 = 5$

$\qquad\qquad t = 6$

4. Solution 1

The equation of the required line is of the form $y = mx + b$.

Since the slope of the line $y = x$ is 1, then a perpendicular line has slope -1 and so $m = -1$.

Since (4, 2) lies on the line, its coordinates satisfy the equation, and so $2 = (-1)(4) + b$; that is, $b = 6$.

Therefore, the equation of the line is $y = -x + 6$ or $x + y = 6$.

Solution 2

Since the line $y = x$ has slope 1, then a perpendicular line has slope -1.

Therefore, the equation of the line with slope -1 that passes through the point (4, 2) is $\dfrac{y - 2}{x - 4} = -1$, or $y = -x + 6$.

5. Solution

Since $BC \perp BA$, then

slope $BC = -\dfrac{1}{\text{slope } BA}$.

Therefore, $\dfrac{y + 3}{-6} = -\dfrac{1}{\dfrac{7}{2}}$

$\dfrac{y + 3}{-6} = -\dfrac{2}{7}$

$y + 3 = \dfrac{12}{7}$

$y = -\dfrac{9}{7}$

The value of y is $-\dfrac{9}{7}$.

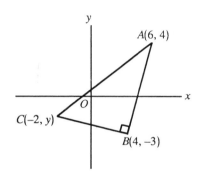

6. Solution

Let the coordinates of the required point be $P(x_1, y_1)$.

From similar triangles AQP and ACB,

$\dfrac{x_1 - 1}{27 - 1} = \dfrac{8}{13}$

and so $x_1 = 17$.

Also, $\dfrac{8 - y_1}{8 - (-5)} = \dfrac{8}{13}$

and so $y_1 = 0$.

Therefore, the point of division is (17, 0).

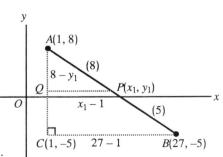

7. Solution

For the line $y = 2x + 1$:

when $x = 1$, $y = 2(1) + 1 = 3$ and

when $x = 5$, $y = 2(5) + 1 = 11$.

The area of trapezoid $ABCD$ is

$\frac{1}{2}(BC)(AB + CD)$

$= \frac{1}{2}(4)(3 + 11)$

$= 2(14)$

$= 28$

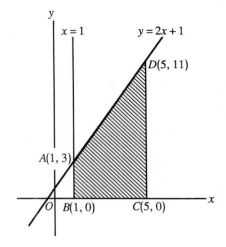

8. Solution

Since slope $AB = \dfrac{OA}{BO} = \dfrac{3}{-4}$,

then slope $AD = \dfrac{ED}{AE} = \dfrac{4}{3}$.

Since $AD = 5$, then $AE = 3$ and $ED = 4$.

Therefore, the coordinates of D are

$(3, 3 + 4) = (3, 7)$.

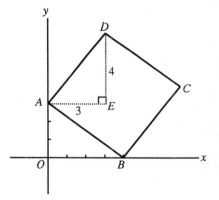

9. Solution 1

The slope of the line $3y - x + 2 = 0$ is $\frac{1}{3}$.

The slope of a line perpendicular to this line is -3 and its equation is

$y + 6 = -3(x - 2)$, or $3x + y = 0$.

Solving $3x + y = 0$ and $x - 3y - 2 = 0$ gives $\left(\frac{1}{5}, -\frac{3}{5}\right)$ as the point of intersection.

Solution 2

Let the coordinates of the foot of the
perpendicular from P be $Q(a, b)$.
Since Q lies on the line $3y - x + 2 = 0$,
then $3b - a + 2 = 0$.   (1)
Since the slope of $3y - x + 2 = 0$ is $\frac{1}{3}$,
then the slope of PQ is -3.
Therefore, $\dfrac{b + 6}{a - 2} = -3$
$3a + b = 0$ (2)
Solving (1) and (2) gives $a = \frac{1}{5}$, $b = -\frac{3}{5}$.
The point Q is $\left(\frac{1}{5}, -\frac{3}{5}\right)$.

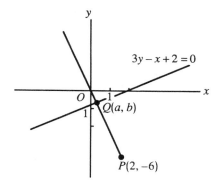

10. Solution

The line $y = mx - 4$ intersects the line $x = 1$
at the point $(1, m - 4)$ and the x-axis at the
point $\left(\frac{4}{m}, 0\right)$.
The area of the triangle is

$$\frac{1}{2}\left(1 - \frac{4}{m}\right)(4 - m) = 9$$
$$8 - m - \frac{16}{m} = 18$$
$$m^2 + 10m + 16 = 0$$
$$(m + 2)(m + 8) = 0$$

Therefore, $m = -2$ or -8.

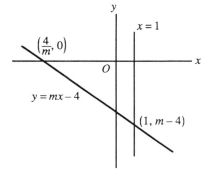

11. Solution

All points equidistant from the x- and y-axes
are on the line $y = x$ or the line $y = -x$.
The required points must be in the first
quadrant since all other points are farther from
$(2, 1)$ than from the coordinate axes.
Let the coordinates of the point be $P(x, y)$.
Now $PA = PB = PC$,
and so $\sqrt{(x - 2)^2 + (y - 1)^2} = x = y$
$$\sqrt{(x - 2)^2 + (x - 1)^2} = x$$
$$x^2 - 4x + 4 + x^2 - 2x + 1 = x^2$$
$$x^2 - 6x + 5 = 0$$
$$(x - 1)(x - 5) = 0$$
$$x = 1 \text{ or } x = 5$$

Therefore, the points satisfying the given conditions are $(1, 1)$ and $(5, 5)$.

12. Solution

Since l_1 and l_2 are parallel they have the same slope.

Let the equation of l_2 be $y = mx + a$.

The coordinates of P are $(0, k)$ and the coordinates of Q are $\left(-\frac{a}{m}, 0\right)$.

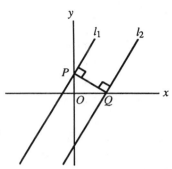

Therefore, slope $PQ = \dfrac{k - 0}{0 + \dfrac{a}{m}} = \dfrac{mk}{a}$.

But slope $PQ = -\dfrac{1}{m}$, since PQ is perpendicular to l_1.

Therefore, $\dfrac{mk}{a} = -\dfrac{1}{m}$

$$a = -km^2$$

Therefore, the y-intercept of line l_2 is $-km^2$.

13. Solution 1

The set of points equidistant from $P(0, 2)$ and $Q(4, 0)$ is the perpendicular bisector of PQ.

This is a line through $(2, 1)$ and having slope $-\dfrac{4}{-2} = 2$.

Its equation is $y - 1 = 2(x - 2)$ or $y = 2x - 3$.

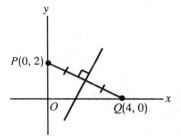

Solution 2

Let $R(x, y)$ be any point that is equidistant from P and Q.

Therefore, $PR = QR$,

and so $\sqrt{x^2 + (y - 2)^2} = \sqrt{(x - 4)^2 + y^2}$.

Squaring gives $x^2 + y^2 - 4y + 4 = x^2 - 8x + 16 + y^2$

$$-4y = -8x + 12$$
$$y = 2x - 3$$

The required equation is $y = 2x - 3$.

14. Solution 1

The area of the given triangle is

$\frac{1}{2}(9)(4) = 18$.

Let the equation of the required
vertical line be $x = a$, and let it
intersect the line through $(0, 0)$ and
$(8, 4)$ at C, and the x-axis at D.
The line through $(0, 0)$ and $(8, 4)$
has equation $\frac{y}{x} = \frac{4}{8}$ or $y = \frac{1}{2}x$.
Since C lies on this line, its
coordinates are $\left(a, \frac{a}{2}\right)$.

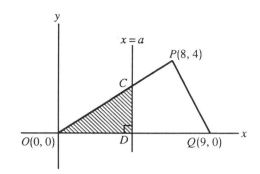

Since the area of $\triangle OCD$ is 9,
then $\frac{1}{2}(a)\left(\frac{a}{2}\right) = 9$

$$a^2 = 36$$
$$a = \pm 6$$

But $a = -6$ is inadmissible since C is in the first quadrant.
The required line has equation $x = 6$.

Solution 2

Let the vertical line cut the line segment OP at C and the x-axis at D.
Since the slopes of OC and OP are equal, the coordinates of C and D can be
expressed as $(2k, k)$ and $(2k, 0)$, respectively.

Since the area of $\triangle OCD$ is 9, then $\frac{1}{2}(2k)(k) = 9$

$$k^2 = 9$$
$$k = \pm 3$$

But $k = -3$ is inadmissible, since C is in the first quadrant.
Therefore, the required equation is $x = 6$.

15. Solution

The lines $y = 3x + 1$ and $y = 4$ intersect at
$(1, 4)$.
Since $y = 3x + 1$ passes through $(0, 1)$, its
image passes through $(0, 7)$.

The slope of the reflected line is $\frac{7-4}{0-1} = -3$.

Therefore, its equation is $y = -3x + 7$.

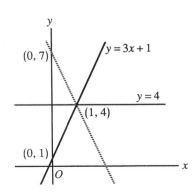

16. Solution 1

Let a typical member of the family have equation $ax + by + c = 0$.

The intercepts of this line on the x- and y-axes are $-\frac{c}{a}$ and $-\frac{c}{b}$, respectively, and it is

given that $-\frac{a}{c} + \left(-\frac{b}{c}\right) = k$ (a constant).

Thus, $-a - b = ck$, or $c = -\frac{a+b}{k}$.

Now the equation of the line can be written as

$$ax + by - \frac{a+b}{k} = 0,$$

$$\text{or } a\left(x - \frac{1}{k}\right) + b\left(y - \frac{1}{k}\right) = 0.$$

This shows that the point $P\left(\frac{1}{k}, \frac{1}{k}\right)$ lies on the typical member of the family.

Since P is a fixed point, all members of the family pass through this same point P.

Solution 2

Let a and b be the x- and y-intercepts of a general line.

Then the line has equation $\frac{x}{a} + \frac{y}{b} = 1$.

Also, it is given that $\frac{1}{a} + \frac{1}{b} = k$; that is,

$$\frac{\left(\frac{1}{k}\right)}{a} + \frac{\left(\frac{1}{k}\right)}{b} = 1.$$

This equation shows that $P\left(\frac{1}{k}, \frac{1}{k}\right)$ satisfies the line equation, that is, lies on the line.

Since P is a fixed point, all members of the family pass through the point P.

17. Solution

The lines $3x + 2y = 30$ and $2x + 3y = 30$
intersect at $(6, 6)$.

The line $3x + 2y = 30$ cuts the x-axis at
$(10, 0)$; the line $2x + 3y = 30$ cuts the y-axis
at $(0, 10)$.

Hence, the figure can be considered as two
triangles, each with base 10 and height 6, and
the area is $2\left(\frac{1}{2} \times 10 \times 6\right) = 60$.

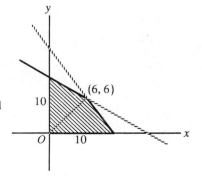

18. <u>Solution</u>

Since $\triangle ABC$ is an isosceles triangle
and $\angle BAC = 90°$, then $AB = AC$.
Let the coordinates of B be (h, k).
Since C is the image of B after a
rotation of $90°$ about the origin, the
coordinates of C are $(-k, h)$.
Since points B and C are on the given
line,

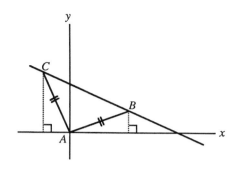

$$2(h) + 3(k) - 13 = 0$$
and $\quad 2(-k) + 3(h) - 13 = 0$
Thus, $4h + 6k = 26$ $\qquad$ (1)
and $\quad 9h - 6k = 39$ $\qquad$ (2)
Adding (1) and (2): $\quad 13h = 65$
$$h = 5, \text{ and so } k = 1.$$
The coordinates of B and C are $(5, 1)$ and
$(-1, 5)$, respectively.

19. <u>Solution</u>

Let coordinate axes lie along AB and AC.
Then the coordinates of B are $(12, 0)$.
Let the coordinates of C be $(0, 2b)$.
Since D and E are the midpoints of AC and
BC, their coordinates are $(0, b)$ and $(6, b)$,
respectively.
Since $AE \perp BD$, the product of their slopes
is -1.

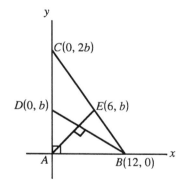

Hence, $\left(\dfrac{b}{6}\right)\left(\dfrac{-b}{12}\right) = -1$
$$b^2 = 72$$
Therefore, $(BC)^2 = (AC)^2 + (AB)^2$
$$= 4b^2 + 144$$
$$= 4(72) + 144$$
$$= 432$$
Hence, $BC = \sqrt{432}$
$$= 12\sqrt{3}$$

20. <u>Solution 1</u>

The image of the point (x, y) when
reflected in the line $y = -x$ is
$(u, v) = (-y, -x)$.
Hence, $x = -v$ and $y = -u$.
The equation of the reflected line is

$$2(-v) - 3(-u) + 6 = 0$$
$$3u - 2v + 6 = 0$$

or $3x - 2y + 6 = 0$ in the xy-plane.
The image of the reflected line has equation
$3x - 2y + 6 = 0$.

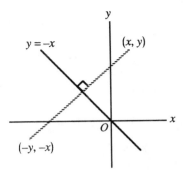

<u>Solution 2</u>

Two points on the given line are $(-3, 0)$ and $(0, 2)$.
Their images, when reflected in the line $y = -x$, are $(0, 3)$ and $(-2, 0)$, respectively.
The equation of the image line is $\dfrac{y - 3}{x - 0} = \dfrac{0 - 3}{-2 - 0}$ or $3x - 2y + 6 = 0$.

21. <u>Solution</u>

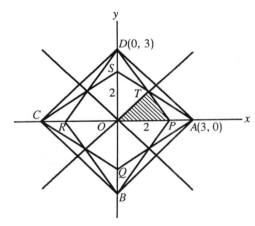

Let the coordinate axes fall along CA and BD, respectively.
By symmetry, the area common to parallelograms $AQCS$ and $BRDP$ is 8 times the
area of $\triangle OTP$.
Let the coordinates of A and D be $(3, 0)$ and $(0, 3)$, respectively.
Thus, the coordinates of P are $(2, 0)$ and the coordinates of S are $(0, 2)$.
The equation of the line containing PD is $y = -\dfrac{3}{2}x + 3$ and the equation of the line
containing SA is $y = -\dfrac{2}{3}x + 2$.

Solving these two equations gives the point of intersection, $T\left(\frac{6}{5}, \frac{6}{5}\right)$.

The area of $\triangle OTP = \frac{1}{2}(2)\left(\frac{6}{5}\right) = \frac{6}{5}$.

Since the length of AD is $\sqrt{18}$, the area of square $ABCD$ is 18.

The ratio of the area common to parallelograms $AQCS$ and $BRDP$ to the area of square $ABCD$ is $\frac{48}{5}:18 = 8:15$.

22. Solution

The length of perpendicular PA from $P(-1, -2)$ to the line $x + 2y - 5 = 0$ is

$$PA = \frac{|-1 + 2(-2) - 5|}{\sqrt{1^2 + 2^2}}$$

$$= \frac{10}{\sqrt{5}}$$

$$= 2\sqrt{5}$$

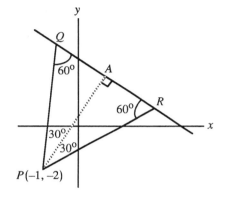

Since the sides of a 30°-60°-90° triangle are in the ratio $1:\sqrt{3}:2$, then

$$\frac{PA}{PQ} = \frac{\sqrt{3}}{2}$$

$$\frac{2\sqrt{5}}{PQ} = \frac{\sqrt{3}}{2}$$

$$PQ = \frac{4\sqrt{5}}{\sqrt{3}} = \frac{4\sqrt{15}}{3}$$

The length of a side of the equilateral triangle is $\frac{4\sqrt{15}}{3}$.

23. Solution

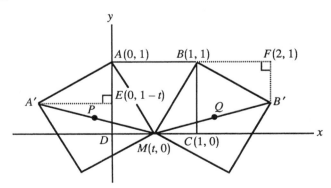

Without loss of generality, let the points be $A(0, 1)$, $B(1, 1)$, $C(1, 0)$, and $D(0, 0)$.

Let M be the point $(t, 0)$, with $0 \le t \le 1$.

Since $\triangle A'EA \equiv \triangle ADM$, the coordinates of A' are $(-1, 1 - t)$.

Since $\triangle BFB' \equiv \triangle BCM$, the coordinates of B' are $(2, t)$.

Since P and Q are the centres of the constructed squares, the coordinates of P are $\left(\dfrac{t-1}{2}, \dfrac{1-t}{2}\right)$ and the coordinates of Q are $\left(\dfrac{2+t}{2}, \dfrac{t}{2}\right)$. The midpoint of PQ is $\left(\dfrac{1+2t}{4}, \dfrac{1}{4}\right)$ for $0 \le t \le 1$. The path of the midpoint of PQ is the line segment joining the points $\left(\dfrac{1}{4}, \dfrac{1}{4}\right)$ and $\left(\dfrac{3}{4}, \dfrac{1}{4}\right)$.

24. Solution 1

$|x| + |x - 2| + |y| = 6$

There are 8 cases to consider of which only 6 give consistent results.

(i) $x \ge 2, y \ge 0$

     $x + (x - 2) + y = 6$

     $y = -2x + 8$

(ii) $x \ge 2, y < 0$

     $x + (x - 2) - y = 6$

     $y = 2x - 8$

(iii) $0 \le x < 2, y \ge 0$

     $x - (x - 2) + y = 6$

     $y = 4$

(iv) $0 \le x < 2, y < 0$

     $x - (x - 2) - y = 6$

     $y = -4$

(v) $x < 0, y \ge 0$

     $-x - (x - 2) + y = 6$

     $y = 2x + 4$

(vi) $x < 0, y < 0$

     $-x - (x - 2) - y = 6$

     $y = -2x - 4$

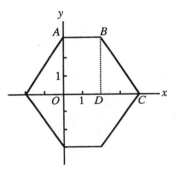

The area of the region bounded by these six line segments is

2(rectangle $ABDO$) + 4(triangle BDC)

     $= 2(8) + 4(4)$

     $= 32$

Solution 2

$|x| + |x-2| + |y| = 6$

(i)   If $x < 0$, the equation becomes

$-x - (x-2) + |y| = 6$

$|y| = 2x + 4$

If $y \geq 0$, we obtain $y = 2x + 4$.

If $y < 0$, we obtain $y = -2x - 4$.

(ii)   If $0 \leq x < 2$ the equation becomes

$x - (x-2) + |y| = 6$

$|y| = 4$

From this we obtain equations $y = 4$ and $y = -4$.

(iii)   If $x \geq 2$, the equation becomes

$x + (x-2) + |y| = 6$

$|y| = -2x + 8$

This gives the equations $y = -2x + 8$ and $y = 2x - 8$.

In each case we obtain a pair of line segments whose graphs are reflections of one another in the x-axis as illustrated in the diagram.

The area of the region bounded by these six lines is

$2(\text{trapezoid } ABCE) = 2\left(\frac{1}{2}\right)(2 + 6)(4)$

$= 32$

25. Solution

Using trial and error, the given equation can be factored:

$6x^2 + xy - 2y^2 + 11x + 5y + 3 = 0$

$(3x + 2y + 1)(2x - y + 3) = 0$

$3x + 2y + 1 = 0$ or $2x - y + 3 = 0$

Therefore, the product of the slopes of the two straight lines is $\left(-\frac{3}{2}\right)\left(\frac{2}{1}\right) = -3$.

Note: In general, if $A_1 x + B_1 y + C_1 = 0$ and $A_2 x + B_2 y + C_2 = 0$ represent two

straight lines, the product of their slopes is $\left(-\frac{A_1}{B_1}\right)\left(\frac{A_2}{-B_2}\right) = \frac{A_1 A_2}{B_1 B_2}$.

But $(A_1 x + B_1 y + C_1)(A_2 x + B_2 y + C_2) = 0$ yields $(A_1 A_2 x^2 + B_1 B_2 y^2 + ...) = 0$.

Therefore, the required product of slopes is $\frac{6}{-2} = -3$.

Properties of Integers

1. <u>Solution</u>

In a perfect square every prime factor occurs an even number of times.

We note that $54 = 2 \times 3^3$.

Thus, if the product is to be a square, 54 must be multiplied by $2 \times 3 = 6$.

2. <u>Solution</u>

Since p, q, r are consecutive integers with $p < q < r$, then we can write $q = p + 1$ and $r = p + 2$.

Then $a = p + r = 2p + 2 = 2(p + 1)$

$b = pr = p(p + 2) = p^2 + 2p$

$c = r - p = p + 2 - p = 2$

Thus, a and c are always even, and b is even when p is even, but odd when p is odd.

3. <u>Solution</u>

Let the number be $(abc)_7$ with a, b, c integers such that $1 \le a \le 6$ and $0 \le b, c \le 6$.

Then $(abc)_7 = (cba)_9$.

Now $(abc)_7 = a \cdot 7^2 + b \cdot 7 + c$

$= 49a + 7b + c$

$(cba)_9 = c \cdot 9^2 + b \cdot 9 + a$

$= 81c + 9b + a$

Then $49a + 7b + c = 81c + 9b + a$

or $24a - b - 40c = 0$

Since the maximum value of $24a$ is 144, $c \le 3$, and since 4 divides both $24a$ and $40c$, then b is either 0 or 4.

Now if $c = 0$, $24a - b = 0$ and this is impossible since a is a positive integer and $b = 0$ or $b = 4$.

If $c = 1$, $24a - b = 40$, and there is no integer value for a if $b = 0$ or $b = 4$.

If $c = 2$, $24a - b = 80$, and again there is no integer value for a if $b = 0$ or $b = 4$.

If $c = 3$, $24a - b = 120$, and there is no integer value for a if $b = 4$.

However, if $b = 0$, $a = 5$.

The only three digit base 7 number satisfying the condition is $(503)_7$.

4. <u>Solution</u>

The sum of all pairs $(a + b) + (a + c) + (a + d) + ... + (d + e)$ contains each of the numbers four times.

Hence, $4(a + b + c + d + e) = 1912$

$a + b + c + d + e = 478$

Since $a + b$ is the smallest sum, then $a + b = 183$, and since $d + e$ is the largest sum then $d + e = 200$.

Hence, $c = 478 - 183 - 200 = 95$.

Now $a + c$ is the second smallest sum, so $a + c = 186$.

Therefore, $a = 91$.

5. Solution 1

$7^1 = 7$, $7^2 = 49$, $7^3 = 343$, $7^4 = 2301$

$7^5 = \ldots 07$, $7^6 = \ldots 49$, $7^7 = \ldots 43$, $7^8 = \ldots 01$

This is a cyclic pattern of repeating last two digits, with a cycle of 4. Note that $1989 = 4 \times 497 + 1$, and that 7^{1989} must be the first in a set of four powers of 7. Hence, the last two digits are 07.

Solution 2

$7^1 \equiv 07 \pmod{100}$, $7^2 \equiv 49 \pmod{100}$, $7^3 \equiv 43 \pmod{100}$, $7^4 \equiv 01 \pmod{100}$

Since $1989 \equiv 1 \pmod 4$, then $7^{1989} \equiv 7^1 \pmod{100} \equiv 07 \pmod{100}$.

The last two digits are 07.

6. Solution

In the first class the average mark of a_1 out of a possible n_1 marks can be changed to an average of $\dfrac{100a_1}{n_1}$ out of 100 (that is, to a percentage).

Similarly, the second class has an average of $\dfrac{100a_2}{n_2}$ out of 100.

Thus, the total in marks out of 100, awarded to the two classes is $\dfrac{100a_1m_1}{n_1} + \dfrac{100a_2m_2}{n_2}$.

Since the number of students involved is $m_1 + m_2$, the average, as a percent, is

$$\frac{\dfrac{100a_1m_1}{n_1} + \dfrac{100a_2m_2}{n_2}}{m_1 + m_2}, \text{ or } 100\,\frac{a_1m_1n_2 + a_2m_2n_1}{n_1n_2(m_1 + m_2)}.$$

7. Solution

Every odd integer is of the form $2n + 1$ where n is an integer.

Then $(2n + 1)^2 = 4n^2 + 4n + 1$

$$= 4(n^2 + n) + 1$$
$$= 4(n)(n + 1) + 1$$

Since n and $n + 1$ are consecutive integers, one of them is a multiple of 2.

Hence, $4(n)(n + 1)$ is divisible by 8 and can be written as $8q$.

Thus, the square of any odd integer can be expressed in the form $8q + 1$.

8. <u>Solution</u>

    Let the positive integers be x and $x + 2$.

    Then $(x + 2)^2 - x^2 = 4x + 4 = n^2$.

    Hence, $n = 2\sqrt{x + 1}$.

    Since n is an integer, $x + 1$ is a perfect square.

    Thus, $x + 1 = 1, 4, 9, ..., k^2, ...$ where k is a positive integer and $x = 3, 8, 15, ..., (k^2 - 1), ...,$ since $x = 0$ is not positive.

    Hence, $n = 4, 6, 8, 10, ..., 2k, ...$ where k is an integer, $k \geq 2$.

9. <u>Solution</u>

    $$n^5 - 5n^3 + 4n = n(n^4 - 5n^2 + 4)$$
    $$= n(n^2 - 1)(n^2 - 4)$$
    $$= n(n - 1)(n + 1)(n - 2)(n + 2)$$

    This is the product of five consecutive integers for n a positive integer. Of any five consecutive positive integers, at least one is a multiple of 4 and at least one other is even or a multiple of 2.

    Hence, the given expression is divisible by 8 for all positive integers n.

10. <u>Solution</u>

    Let $T = mn(m^4 - n^4)$
    $$= mn(m^2 - n^2)(m^2 + n^2)$$
    $$= mn(m - n)(m + n)(m^2 + n^2)$$

    We shall prove that T is divisible by 2, 3, and 5.

    First, if either m or n is even, then T is even. If both m and n are odd, then $m + n$ is even, and T is even.

    Hence, T is divisible by 2.

    Second, if either m or n is a multiple of 3, then T is divisible by 3. If neither is a multiple of 3, then we can write $m = 3p \pm 1$, $n = 3q \pm 1$, for p and q integers.

    If m and n have like signs in these expressions, then $m - n$ is a multiple of 3, while if the signs are unlike, then $m + n$ is a multiple of 3.

    Hence, T is divisible by 3.

    Lastly, if either m or n is a multiple of 5, then T is divisible by 5. If neither is a multiple of 5, we write $m = 5p \pm 1$ or $5p \pm 2$ and $n = 5q \pm 1$ or $5q \pm 2$, where p and q are integers.

    Note that $(5p \pm 1)^2 = 25p^2 \pm 10p + 1 = 5(5p^2 \pm 2p) + 1$, and we can set $m^2 = 5h + 1$, while $(5p \pm 2)^2 = 25p^2 \pm 20p + 4$ and we can set $m^2 = 5k - 1$.

    Similarly, $n^2 = 5r + 1$ or $n^2 = 5s - 1$, where $h, k, r, s,$ are integers.

    It follows that either $m^2 - n^2$ or $m^2 + n^2$ is a multiple of 5, and hence T is divisible by 5.

    Since T is divisible by 2, 3, and 5, it is divisible by 30.

11. Solution 1

Since both p and q are odd we get $q = p + 2k$, where k is a positive integer.

Then, $p + q = p + (p + 2k) = 2(p + k)$.

Now $p + k$ lies between p and q, and hence it is not prime.

We conclude that $p + k$ has at least two factors, and hence that $p + q$ has at least three prime factors.

Solution 2

Since p and q are both odd, $p + q$ is even. Solve $p + q = 2r$.

Now, if $p < q$, $\dfrac{p+q}{2} > \dfrac{p+p}{2} = p$, and $\dfrac{p+q}{2} < \dfrac{q+q}{2} = q$.

Therefore, $p < r < q$.

But p and q are consecutive odd primes and so r is composite.

Hence, $2r$ has at least three prime factors.

12. Solution

$$m^4 + 4n^4 = m^4 + 4m^2n^2 + 4n^4 - 4m^2n^2$$
$$= (m^2 + 2n^2)^2 - (2mn)^2$$
$$= (m^2 - 2mn + 2n^2)(m^2 + 2mn + 2n^2)$$

Now if $m^4 + 4n^4$ is prime, it has no factors other than 1 and itself.

Of the two factors of $m^4 + 4n^4$, the smaller is $m^2 - 2mn + 2n^2$ and its value must be 1.

We obtain $m^2 - 2mn + 2n^2 = (m^2 - 2mn + n^2) + n^2$
$$= (m - n)^2 + n^2$$
$$= 1$$

This is possible only for $m = n = 1$.

Hence, the only solution is $m = n = 1$.

13. Solution

Note that $2^{10} = 1024 > 10^3$.

Hence, $2^{3217} = (2^{10})^{321} \cdot 2^7 > (10^3)^{321} \cdot 2^7$
$$> 10^{963} \cdot 10^2$$
$$> 10^{965}$$

So 2^{3217} contains at least 965 digits.

Now $2^{13} = 8192 < 10^4$.

Hence, $2^{3217} = (2^{13})^{247} \cdot 2^6 < (10^4)^{247} \cdot 2^6$
$$< 10^{988} \cdot 10^2$$
$$< 10^{990}$$

So 2^{3217} contains at most 990 digits.

Therefore, $965 \le n \le 990$.

14. Solution 1

$16^n = (15 + 1)^n$

$$= 15^n + \binom{n}{1} 15^{n-1} + \binom{n}{2} 15^{n-2} + \ldots + \binom{n}{n-2} 15^2 + \binom{n}{n-1} 15 + 1$$

$$= 5^2 3^2 \left[15^{n-2} + \binom{n}{1} 15^{n-3} + \binom{n}{2} 15^{n-4} + \ldots + \binom{n}{n-2} \right] + 15n + 1$$

$$= 25m + 15n + 1$$

Hence, $16^n + 10n - 1 = 25m + 15n + 10n - 1 + 1$
$$= 25(m + n)$$

The expression is divisible by 25.

Solution 2

If $n = 1$, then $16^n + 10n - 1 = 16 + 10 - 1 = 25$.

The assertion is true for $n = 1$.

Assume that for $n = k$ the assertion holds, and so $f(k) = 16^k + 10k - 1$ is divisible by 25 for $k \geq 1$.

Then $f(k + 1) = 16^{k+1} + 10(k + 1) - 1$
$$= 16(16^k) + 160k - 150k + 25 - 16$$
$$= 16(16k + 10k - 1) - 150k + 25$$
$$= 16f(k) - 25(6k - 1)$$

Hence, $f(k + 1)$ is a multiple of 25.

Since the statement holds for $n = 1$, and holds for $n = k + 1$ whenever it holds for $n = k$, then, by the principle of mathematical induction, the statement is true for all positive integers.

15. Solution 1

If $f(x) = \dfrac{x^5}{5} + \dfrac{x^3}{3} + \dfrac{7x}{15}$, then $f(1) = \dfrac{1}{5} + \dfrac{1}{3} + \dfrac{7}{15} = 1$.

Hence, $f(1)$ is an integer.

Assume that $f(k)$ is an integer for $x = k$ where k is a positive integer.

Then $f(k + 1) = \dfrac{(k + 1)^5}{5} + \dfrac{(k + 1)^3}{3} + \dfrac{7(k + 1)}{15}$

$$= \frac{k^5}{5} + k^4 + 2k^3 + 2k^2 + k + \frac{1}{5} + \frac{k^3}{3} + k^2 + k + \frac{1}{3} + \frac{7k}{15} + \frac{7}{15}$$

$$= \frac{k^5}{5} + \frac{k^3}{3} + \frac{7k}{15} + k^4 + 2k^3 + 3k^2 + 2k + 1$$

$$= f(k) + k^4 + 2k^3 + 3k^2 + 2k + 1$$

Now if k is an integer, $k^4 + 2k^3 + 3k^2 + 2k + 1$ is an integer, and hence, if $f(k)$ is an integer, $f(k + 1)$ is an integer.

Therefore, $f(1)$ is an integer, and whenever $f(k)$ is an integer so is $f(k + 1)$. By the principle of mathematical induction, $f(k)$ is an integer for all positive integral values of x.

Solution 2

$$f(x) = \frac{x^5}{5} + \frac{x^3}{3} + \frac{7x}{15} = \frac{3x^5 + 5x^3 + 7x}{15}$$

Now $x^5 = x(x^2 - 1)(x^2 - 4) + 5x^3 - 4x$

$$= (x - 2)(x - 1)x(x + 1)(x + 2) + 5x^3 - 4x$$

and $x^3 = x(x^2 - 1) + x$

$$= (x - 1)(x)(x + 1) + x$$

Thus, $3x^5 + 5x^3 + 7x$

$$= 3(x - 2)(x - 1)x(x + 1)(x + 2) + 5(x - 1)x(x + 1) + 7x + 15^3 - 12x + 5x$$

$$= 3(x - 2)(x - 1)x(x + 1)(x + 2) + 5(x - 1)x(x + 1) + 15x^3$$

Now, of five consecutive numbers, one is a multiple of 5, so
$3(x - 2)(x - 1)x(x + 1)(x + 2)$ is divisible by 15.

Similarly, of three consecutive numbers, one is a multiple of 3, so $5(x - 1)x(x + 1)$ is divisible by 15.

Thus, $3x^5 + 5x^3 + 7x$ is divisible by 15, and $\dfrac{3x^5 + 5x^3 + x}{15}$ is an integer.

16. Solution

Since x_1 is even and x_2 is odd, then $x_3 = x_2 + x_1$ is odd. $x_4 = x_3 + x_2$, which is even. Similarly x_5 and x_6 are odd, x_7 is even, x_8 and x_9 are odd, etc.

Thus, the pattern of the digits will be *.EOOEOOEOO...* where E represents an even digit and O represents an odd digit. Since there are only 25 different EO sequences, (E can be any one of 5 even digits and O can be any one of 5 odd digits), the same EOO sequence must appear twice within the first 26 EOO triples.

Hence, A is a repeating decimal and is rational.

17. Solution

Suppose that there is a set of k consecutive positive integers $m, m + 1, m + 2, ...,$ $m + k - 1$, with $k > 1$, which has sum equal to a power of 2.

Then $m + (m + 1) + (m + 2) + ... + (m + k - 1) = 2^t$, t an integer.

$$2^t = km + (1 + 2 + 3 + ... + k - 1)$$

$$= km + \frac{(k - 1)k}{2}$$

Hence, $2^{t+1} = 2km + k(k - 1)$

$$= k(2m + k - 1)$$

Hence, $k(2m + k - 1)$ is an even number (a power of 2). This means that, since $k > 1$, k is even and $2m + k - 1$ is also even. But $2m$ is certainly even, so $k - 1$ is also even. However, it is impossible for both k and $k - 1$ to be even, so there is a contradiction, and the supposition is rejected. We conclude that there is no set of consecutive positive integers whose sum is a power of 2.

18. Solution 1

Observe that $1441 = 11 \times 131$. If the expression is divisible by 1441, it is divisible by both 11 and 131.

Now $60 \equiv 5 \pmod{11}$ and $71 \equiv 5 \pmod{11}$, and $5^n \not\equiv 0 \pmod{11}$. [That is, 5^n is never divisible by 11.]

Hence, $60^n + k(71^n) \equiv 5^n (1 + k) \pmod{11}$

$$\equiv 0 \pmod{11}$$

Then $1 + k = 11l$, l an integer, and $k = 11l - 1$.

Similarly, $60 \equiv -71 \pmod{131}$ and $71^n \not\equiv 0 \pmod{131}$, so

$$60^n + k(71^n) \equiv 71^n(-1 + k) \pmod{131} \equiv 0 \pmod{131}.$$

Then $-1 + k = 131t$, t an integer and $k = 131t + 1$.

Equating the two values for k,

$$11l - 1 = 131t + 1$$
$$l = \frac{131t + 2}{11}$$

Setting $t = 2$ gives $l = 24$ and $k = 263$ and this is the smallest value possible (in positive integers).

Solution 2

Observe that $1441 = 11 \times 131$.

Hence, 11 divides $60^n + k \cdot 71^n$ and 131 divides $60^n + k \cdot 71^n$.

From the first of these we write

$$60^n + k \cdot 71^n = (60^n - 71^n) + (k + 1) 71^n$$

and since $60^n - 71^n$ is divisible by 11 (by the Factor Theorem), then $(k + 1) 71^n$ is divisible by 11. But 71^n is not divisible by 11, so $k + 1$ is divisible by 11 and we write $k + 1 = 11l$, l an integer.

Similarly, $60^n + k \cdot 71^n = 60^n + 71^n + (k - 1) 71^n$ and by the Factor Theorem $60^n + 71^n$ is divisible by 131 for odd values of n (but not for even values). By the same process as before, we write $k - 1 = 131t$, t an integer.

The remainder of the solution is the same as Solution 1.

19. Solution

Consider p as odd, since the only even prime is $p = 2$. Then we can write the product of the primes as

$$(2)(3)(5)(7)(11)...(p) < (2)(3)(4)(5)...(p)$$
$$= p!$$

$$p! = (2)(p) \cdot (3)(p - 1) \cdot (4)(p - 2)....$$

$$= \prod_{i=2}^{\frac{p+1}{2}} i(p + 2 - i)$$

where there are $\frac{p-1}{2}$ pairs each with sum $p + 2$. Note that there is always such a pairing since p is odd. Now for a and b positive integers, the arithmetic-geometric mean inequality gives

$$ab \leq \left(\frac{a+b}{2}\right)^2$$

Hence, for $a = i$, $b = p + 2 - i$, we obtain

$$i(p + 2 - i) \leq \left(\frac{p+2}{2}\right)^2.$$

Hence, $p! \leq \left[\left(\frac{p+2}{2}\right)^2\right]^{\frac{p-1}{2}} = \left(\frac{p+2}{2}\right)^{p-1}.$

Finally, combining the statements we have

$$(2)\,(3)\,(5)...(p) < p! \leq \left(\frac{p+2}{2}\right)^{p-1}.$$

20. Solution

Assume that, for a and b positive integers,

$$b^2 = a(a + 1)(a + 2)$$

Since $a + 1$ differs from each of a and $a + 2$ by 1 it is relatively prime to each. That is, there are no factors in common between $a + 1$ and either a or $a + 2$.

Therefore, $a + 1$ must be a square and $a(a + 2)$ must also be a square.

Hence, we write $a^2 + 2a = t^2$, for a positive integer t.

But $t^2 > a^2$ and $t^2 < a^2 + 2a + 1 = (a + 1)^2$.

Thus, $a < t < a + 1$.

But this is impossible since a and $a + 1$ are consecutive integers. Hence the assumption is false.

Therefore, the product of three consecutive positive integers cannot be a perfect square.

21. Solution

There are three possible cases for x and y: both odd, one odd and one even, and both even. (Note that since x and y appear symmetrically, the second case is completely argued for x odd, y even.)

Case 1

Both x and y odd.

Then xy is also odd and hence z is odd.

Accordingly, let $x = 2a + 1$, $y = 2b + 1$, $z = 2c + 1$, and $xy = 2d + 1$ where a, b, c, and d are integers.

Substituting in the equation gives

$$4a^2 + 4a + 1 + 4b^2 + 4b + 1 + 4c^2 + 4c + 1 = 4d^2 + 4d + 1$$
$$4(a^2 + a + b^2 + b + c^2 + c - d^2 - d) = -2$$

This is impossible since the left side is divisible by 4 while the right side is not.

<u>Case 2</u>

x odd, y even.

Then xy is even and z must be odd.

Let $x = 2a + 1$, $y = 2b$, $z = 2c + 1$, $xy = 2d$, and substitute to obtain

$$4(a^2 + a + b^2 + c^2 + c - d^2) = -2$$

As in case 1, this is an impossible situation.

<u>Case 3</u>

Both x and y even.

Then z is even, as is xy.

Every even number can be written as a power of 2 multiplied by an odd number (e.g.

$56 = 2^3 \times 7$, $142 = 2^1 \times 71$). Let $x = 2^a u$, $y = 2^b v$, $z = 2^c w$, $xy = 2^{a+b} uv$, where u, v,

and w are odd.

Now the equation becomes

$$4^a u^2 + 4^b v^2 + 4^c w^2 = 4^{a+b} u^2 v^2$$

Since each of a, b, c is at least one, there are four cases to consider.

If $a = b = c$, dividing by 4^a gives $u^2 + v^2 + w^2 = 4^a u^2 v^2$.

This is impossible since the left side is odd while the right side is even.

If $a < b < c$, dividing by 4^a gives $u^2 + 4^{b-a} v^2 + 4^{c-a} w^2 = 4^b u^2 v^2$, which is

impossible for the same reason. Any other form of the inequality gives the same

result.

If $a = b > c$, dividing by 4^c gives the same result as the last case, as does $a < b = c$

or $b < a = c$.

If $a = b < c$, dividing by 4^a gives $u^2 + v^2 + 4^{c-a} w^2 = 4^b u^2 v^2$. Now $u^2 + v^2$ is the

sum of two odd integers and is divisible by 2 but not by 4, while $4^b u^2 v^2 - 4^{c-a} w^2$ is

divisible by 4. As in Case 1 above, this is impossible.

The same result follows for $a > b = c$ or $b > a = c$.

Since all cases are exhausted, we conclude there are no positive integers satisfying the

given condition.

Miscellaneous Problems

1. Solution 1

    Let $CT = d$ be the diameter of the wheel.

    Because CT is a diameter, $\angle CAT$ is a right angle.

    Because $CT \parallel AB$, $\angle CTA = \angle TAB$.

    We note that $\angle ABT$ is a right angle.

    Hence, $\triangle CTA$ is similar to $\triangle TAB$ and $\dfrac{CT}{AT} = \dfrac{AT}{AB}$.

    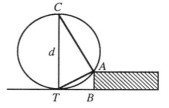

    It follows that $d = \dfrac{(AT)^2}{AB}$.

    Solution 2

    Since CT is a diameter, $\angle CAT = 90°$.

    Since TB is a tangent and AT is a chord, $\angle TCA = \angle ATB$.

    $d = AT \csc \angle TCA$

    $\quad = AT \csc \angle ATB$

    $\quad = AT \cdot \dfrac{AT}{AB}$

    $\quad = \dfrac{(AT)^2}{AB}$

2. Solution

    Since $2^6 + m^n = 2^7$, then $m^n = 2^7 - 2^6 = 64$.

    The possible forms of m^n are 2^6, 4^3, 8^2, and 64^1.

    The possible values of x are 8, 7, 10, and 65.

    The sum of all possible values of x is 90.

3. Solution

    The amount of light transmitted by each circle can be determined by finding the area of the unshaded portion of each circle.

    Let the area of the shaded region be A.

    Then the larger circle transmits $(\pi a^2 - A)L$ lumens and the smaller circle transmits $(\pi b^2 - A)L$ lumens.

    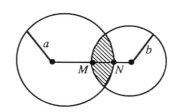

    Since $(\pi a^2 - A)L - (\pi b^2 - A)L = \pi(a^2 - b^2)L$ the larger circle will transmit $\pi(a^2 - b^2)L$ more lumens than the smaller circle.

4. Solution

    The graph of $f(x) = (4x^2 - 9)(x - 1)$
    $$= (2x + 3)(2x - 3)(x - 1)$$
    has x-intercepts $-\frac{3}{2}, \frac{3}{2}$ and 1.
    The function is positive for all values of x for
    which the graph is above the x-axis.
    Hence, $f(x) > 0$ for $-\frac{3}{2} < x < 1$ or $x > \frac{3}{2}$.

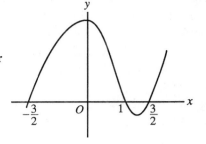

5. Solution 1

    $(x - y + 7)^2 + (x + y - 1)^2 = 0$
    Since $(x - y + 7)^2 \geq 0$ and $(x + y - 1)^2 \geq 0$, the only possibility is
    $$x - y + 7 = 0 \qquad (1)$$
    and $x + y - 1 = 0 \qquad (2)$
    (1) + (2) gives $2x + 6 = 0$
    $$x = -3$$
    (1) − (2) gives $-2y + 8 = 0$
    $$y = 4$$
    Therefore, the solution is $x = -3$, $y = 4$.

    Solution 2

    $$(x - y + 7)^2 + (x + y - 1)^2 = 0$$
    $$x^2 + y^2 + 49 - 2xy + 14x - 14y + x^2 + y^2 + 1 + 2xy - 2x - 2y = 0$$
    $$2x^2 + 2y^2 + 12x - 16y + 50 = 0$$
    $$x^2 + y^2 + 6x - 8y + 25 = 0$$
    $$(x^2 + 6x + 9) + (y^2 - 8y + 16) = -25 + 9 + 16$$
    $$(x + 3)^2 + (y - 4)^2 = 0$$
    This is a "point circle", with centre $(-3, 4)$ and radius 0.
    The only solution is $(x, y) = (-3, 4)$.

6. Solution 1

    Since we want the value of $w + x + y + z$, it is not necessary to solve for each
    variable.
    We observe that twice the first equation added to the second equation added to three
    times the third equation yields $6w + 6x + 6y + 6z = 11\,940$.
    Thus, $w + x + y + z = 1990$.

Solution 2
From the first equation, $2x = 1563 - 6w$.
From the third equation, $y = 1474 + 2w$.
Substitution for x and y in the second equation gives

$$1563 - 6w + 3(1474 + 2w) + 6z = 4392$$

$$z = \frac{-531}{2}$$

Thus, $w + x + y + z = w + \dfrac{1563 - 6w}{2} + (1474 + 2w) + \left(\dfrac{-531}{2}\right)$

$$= 1990$$

7. Solution
    $1! + 2! + 3! + 4! + 5! + \dots + 12!$
    $= 1 + 2 + 6 + 24 + 5! + \dots + 12!$
    $= 33 + 5! + \dots + 12!$
    Since $5!, 6!, \dots, 12!$ each has a factor of 5 and a factor of 2, and hence a factor of 10, each will have units digit of 0 and therefore the units digit in the given sum is 3.

8. Solution
    Since each edge has two endpoints, 21 edges have 42 endpoints.
    Hence, the sum of the degrees of all the vertices is 42.
    Therefore, $6(3) + 4k = 42$

    $$4k = 24$$
    $$k = 6$$

9. Solution
    (a) By completing squares,
        $x^2 + y^2 - 8x + 6y + 20 = 0$ can be
        written in the form
        $(x - 4)^2 + (y + 3)^2 = 5$.
        The curve is a circle with centre
        $C(4, -3)$ and radius $\sqrt{5}$.

    (b) Upon substitution of $(3, -1)$, the left
        side of the given equation has the value
        $9 + 1 - 24 - 6 + 20 = 0$.
        Since the coordinates of A satisfy the
        given equation, the point A lies on the
        circle.

    (c) The radius CA has slope $\dfrac{-1 - (-3)}{3 - 4} = -2$.
        The tangent at A is perpendicular to radius
        CA, and thus has slope $\frac{1}{2}$.

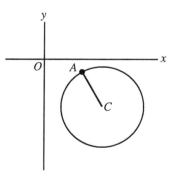

The equation of the required tangent is

$y + 1 = \frac{1}{2}(x - 3)$ or $x - 2y - 5 = 0$.

10. Solution

Let the amounts of salt and water in the solution at the beginning be x and y kilograms respectively.

The fraction of salt in the solution is $\frac{x}{x+y}$.

When one kilogram of salt is added, the fraction of salt in the solution is

$$\frac{x+1}{x+y+1} = \frac{1}{3}. \qquad (1)$$

When one kilogram of water is added, the fraction of salt in the new solution is

$$\frac{x+1}{x+y+2} = \frac{3}{10}. \qquad (2)$$

From the first equation, $3x + 3 = x + y + 1$

$$2x - y = -2 \qquad\qquad (3)$$

From the second equation, $10x + 10 = 3x + 3y + 6$

$$7x - 3y = -4 \qquad\qquad (4)$$

Solving (3) and (4) gives $x = 2, y = 6$.

The percentage of salt in the original solution is $\frac{2}{6+2} \times 100 = 25\%$.

11. Solution 1

$(1^2 + 3^2 + 5^2 + \ldots + 99^2) - (2^2 + 4^2 + 6^2 + \ldots + 100^2) + (4 + 8 + 12 + \ldots + 200)$

$= (1^2 - 2^2 + 4) + (3^2 - 4^2 + 8) + (5^2 - 6^2 + 12) + \ldots + (99^2 - 100^2 + 200)$

$= 1 + 1 + 1 + 1 + \ldots + 1 \qquad$ (50 times)

$= 50(1)$

$= 50$

Solution 2

$(1^2 + 3^2 + 5^2 + \ldots + 99^2) - (2^2 + 4^2 + 6^2 + \ldots + 100^2) + (4 + 8 + 12 + \ldots + 200)$

$= (1^2 + 2^2 + 3^2 + \ldots + 99^2 + 100^2) - 2(2^2 + 4^2 + 6^2 + \ldots + 100^2)$
$\qquad + 4(1 + 2 + 3 + \ldots + 50)$

$= (1^2 + 2^2 + 3^2 + \ldots + 99^2 + 100^2) - 2^3(1 + 2^2 + 3^2 + \ldots + 50^2)$
$\qquad + 4(1 + 2 + 3 + \ldots + 50)$

$= \frac{100(101)(201)}{6} - \frac{8(50)(51)(101)}{6} + \frac{4(50)(51)}{2}$

$= \frac{2\,030\,100}{6} - \frac{2\,060\,400}{6} + \frac{30\,600}{6}$

$= \frac{300}{6}$

$= 50$

12. Solution

Let x be the number of dollars and y the number of cents in the amount on the cheque.

Thus, $100y + x - 350 = 2(100x + y)$

$$199x - 98y = -350$$

$$x = \frac{98y - 350}{199}$$

$$= \frac{14(7y - 25)}{199}$$

Since x is a positive integer, and 14 and 199 are relatively prime, $7y - 25$ is a multiple of 199.

Thus, $7y - 25 = 199t$, where t is an integer

$$7y = 199t + 25$$

Since y is an integer satisfying $0 \le y < 100$, the only possible values of t are 0, 1, 2, and 3.

The only value of t satisfying these conditions is $t = 1$.

Substituting $t = 1$ gives $y = 32$ and $x = 14$.

The cheque was made out for \$14.32.

13. Solution

Since bcd is divisible by 5, $d = 5$.

Since def is divisible by 11, it must be 561.

Since cde is divisible by 3, $c + d + e$ is also divisible by 3.

Therefore, $c = 4$.

Since abc is divisible by 4, $a = 3$ and $b = 2$.

a	b	c	d	e	f
3	2	4	5	6	1

14. Solution

$$\frac{1}{a} + \frac{a}{b} + \frac{1}{ab} = 1$$

Multiply by ab:

$$b + a^2 + 1 = ab$$

$$ab - b = a^2 + 1$$

$$b = \frac{a^2 + 1}{a - 1}$$

$$= a + 1 + \frac{2}{a - 1}$$

Since a and b are positive integers, the only possible values of $a - 1$ are 1 or 2.

These give $a = 2$ or 3.

The solutions are $(a, b) = (2, 5)$ and $(a, b) = (3, 5)$.

15. <u>Solution</u>

The area of quadrilateral *AGHF*

= area of $\triangle OAF$ − area of $\triangle OGH$

$= \frac{1}{2}(5)(5) - \frac{1}{2}(4)(4)$

$= \frac{25}{2} - \frac{16}{2}$

$= \frac{9}{2}$

The area of the shaded quadrilateral

$= \frac{1}{5}$ (area of *AGHF*)

$= \frac{1}{5}\left(\frac{9}{2}\right)$

$= \frac{9}{10}$

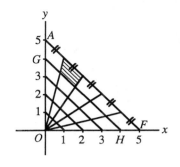

16. <u>Solution</u>

Let $AP = a$, $BQ = b$, $CR = c$ and $DS = d$.

By the theorem of Pythagoras,

$(PQ)^2 + (QR)^2 + (RS)^2 + (SP)^2$

$= (8 - a)^2 + b^2 + (6 - b)^2 + c^2 + (8 - c)^2 + d^2 + (6 - d)^2 + a^2$

$= 200 + 2(a^2 - 8a + b^2 - 6b + c^2 - 8c + d^2 - 6d)$

$= 100 + 2\left[(a - 4)^2 + (b - 3)^2 + (c - 4)^2 + (d - 3)^2\right]$

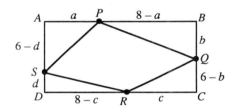

Since each of the perfect squares in the bracket is greater to or equal to zero, the minimum value of the expression is 100. This occurs when *P*, *Q*, *R*, and *S* are the midpoints of the sides of *ABCD*.

Since $0 \le a \le 8$, $0 \le b \le 6$, $0 \le c \le 8$, and $0 \le d \le 6$, the maximum value of the expression is $100 + 2(16 + 9 + 16 + 9) = 200$.

The maximum occurs when *P*, *Q*, *R*, and *S* coincide with *A*, *B*, *C*, and *D* respectively, or with *B*, *C*, *D*, and *A* respectively.

Therefore, $100 \le (PQ)^2 + (QR)^2 + (RS)^2 + (SP)^2 \le 200$.

17. Solution 1

Since $x^3 + y^3 = (x + y)(x^2 - xy + y^2)$, therefore, $8100 = 30(x^2 - xy + y^2)$.

Hence, $x^2 - xy + y^2 = 270$ (1)

Since $x + y = 30$, $x^2 + 2xy + y^2 = 900$ (2)

Adding $2 \times (1)$ to (2) gives $3x^2 + 3y^2 = 1440$

$$x^2 + y^2 = 480$$

Solution 2

$$x^3 + y^3 = (x + y)(x^2 + y^2 - xy)$$
$$= (x + y)[(x + y)^2 - 3xy]$$

Hence, $8100 = 30(900 - 3xy)$

$$3xy = 630$$
$$xy = 210$$

Thus, $x^2 + y^2 = (x + y)^2 - 2xy$

$$= 900 - 420$$
$$= 480$$

18. Solution

Let s km/h be the maximum speed of the train engine when n cars are attached. Then $s = 120 - k\sqrt{n}$, where k is the constant of proportionality.

When $n = 4$, we know $s = 90$.

Therefore, $90 = 120 - k\sqrt{4}$

$$2k = 30$$
$$k = 15$$

We now want to find the value of n so that $s = 0$ (that is, the train can no longer move).

When $s = 0$, $120 - 15\sqrt{n} = 0$

$$\sqrt{n} = 8$$
$$n = 64$$

Hence, with 64 cars, the train will not move.

Therefore, the largest number of cars the train engine can move is 63.

19. <u>Solution 1</u>

Since Y is the midpoint of CD
and Z is the midpoint of AD,
YZ is parallel to and equal to
one half of AC.
Similarly, XW is parallel to and
equal to one half of AC.
Hence, YZ and XW are parallel
and equal, and $WXYZ$ is a
parallelogram in 3-space.
Therefore, the points are
coplanar.

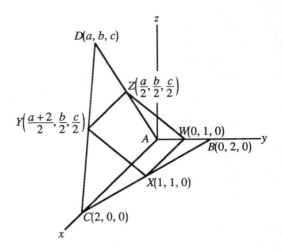

<u>Solution 2</u>

The four midpoints have coordinates $W(0, 1, 0)$, $X(1, 1, 0)$, $Y\left(\frac{a+2}{2}, \frac{b}{2}, \frac{c}{2}\right)$, and $Z\left(\frac{a}{2}, \frac{b}{2}, \frac{c}{2}\right)$.

The length of YZ is $\frac{1}{2}\sqrt{4 + 0 + 0} = 1$ and the direction numbers of YZ are $(-1, 0, 0)$.
Similarly, the length of XW is 1 and its direction numbers are $(-1, 0, 0)$.
Therefore, XW and YZ are equal and parallel line segments.
It follows that X, Y, and W are coplanar since $XYZW$ is a parallelogram.

<u>Solution 3</u>

Using the four points as determined in Solution 2, we let the plane through W, X, and
Z have the equation $Px + Qy + Rz + S = 0$.
Since W, X, and Z are on the plane,

$$Q \qquad\qquad + S = 0 \qquad (1)$$
$$P + Q \qquad\quad + S = 0 \qquad (2)$$
$$\frac{a}{2}P + \frac{b}{2}Q + \frac{c}{2}R + S = 0 \qquad (3)$$

From (1), $Q = -S$.
From (1) and (2), $P = 0$.

From (3), $-\frac{b}{2}S + \frac{c}{2}R + S = 0$

$$R = \frac{b-2}{c}S$$

Hence, the equation of the plane is

$$-Sy + \frac{b-2}{c}Sz + S = 0$$

or $\qquad y - \dfrac{b-2}{c} z - 1 = 0$

Substituting the coordinates of Y, we obtain

$$\dfrac{b}{2} - \dfrac{b-2}{c}\left(\dfrac{c}{2}\right) - 1$$

$$= \dfrac{b}{2} - \dfrac{b}{2} + 1 - 1$$

$$= 0$$

Hence Y is on the plane and the four points are coplanar.

20. <u>Solution 1</u>

The graphs of the square $|x| + |y| = 8$ and the hyperbola $xy = 12$ are illustrated. Since there are four points of intersection, there are four ordered pairs (x, y) in the solution.

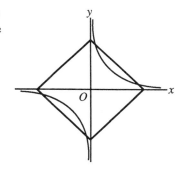

<u>Solution 2</u>

Since $xy = 12$, x and y are either both positive or both negative.

If both are positive, the system becomes $x + y = 8$

$$xy = 12$$

Substitute $y = 8 - x$ in the second equation to give

$$x(8 - x) = 12$$
$$x^2 - 8x + 12 = 0$$
$$(x - 2)(x - 6) = 0$$
$$x = 2 \text{ or } x = 6$$

Therefore, $y = 6$ or $y = 2$.

In this case we obtain the two ordered pairs $(2, 6)$ and $(6, 2)$.

If both are negative, the system becomes $-x - y = 8$

$$xy = 12$$

Solving, we obtain the ordered pairs $(-6, -2)$ and $(-2, -6)$.

Therefore, there are four ordered pairs (x, y) in the solution.

21. Solution 1

(a)   If $\begin{pmatrix} 1 & 3 \\ 4 & 2 \end{pmatrix}\begin{pmatrix} x \\ y \end{pmatrix} = \lambda\begin{pmatrix} x \\ y \end{pmatrix}$,

then $x + 3y = \lambda x$

and $4x + 2y = \lambda y$

This gives two equations $(1 - \lambda)x + 3y = 0$ (1)

and $4x + (2 - \lambda)y = 0$ (2)

(1) × 4: $(4 - 4\lambda)x + 12y = 0$ (3)

(2) × $(1 - \lambda)$: $(4 - 4\lambda)x + (1 - \lambda)(2 - \lambda)y = 0$ (4)

(3) – (4): $[12 - (1 - \lambda)(2 - \lambda)]y = 0$

For non-trivial solutions, $12 - (1 - \lambda)(2 - \lambda) = 0$

$$\lambda^2 - 3\lambda - 10 = 0$$

$$(\lambda - 5)(\lambda + 2) = 0$$

$$\lambda = 5 \text{ or } \lambda = -2$$

(b)   Using $\lambda = 5$ in (1) we obtain $-4x + 3y = 0$ and one solution is $\begin{pmatrix} x \\ y \end{pmatrix} = \begin{pmatrix} 3 \\ 4 \end{pmatrix}$.

Solution 2

Obtain equations (1) and (2) as in Solution 1. This homogeneous system has non-trivial solutions only if the determinent of the coefficients is zero.

$$\begin{vmatrix} 1 - \lambda & 3 \\ 4 & 2 - \lambda \end{vmatrix} = 0$$

$(1 - \lambda)(2 - \lambda) - 12 = 0$

$\lambda^2 - 3\lambda - 10 = 0$

and $\lambda = 5$ or $\lambda = -2$ as before.

Solution 3

Obtain equations (1) and (2) as in Solution 1. From (1) we obtain $\lambda = \dfrac{x + 3y}{x}$ and

from (2) $\lambda = \dfrac{4x + 2y}{y}$.

Hence, $\dfrac{x + 3y}{x} = \dfrac{4x + 2y}{y}$

$4x^2 + xy - 3y^2 = 0$

$(4x - 3y)(x + y) = 0$

If $4x - 3y = 0$, $y = \frac{4}{3}x$ and $\lambda = \dfrac{x + 4x}{x} = 5$.

If $x + y = 0$, $y = -x$ and $\lambda = \dfrac{x - 3x}{x} = -2$.

22. <u>Solution</u>

(a) Consider the straight line with equation $y = mx + b$.
Under the transformation the image coordinates of a point (x, y) on the line are (X, Y), where

$$X = x + 2y$$
$$Y = y$$

Hence, $x = X - 2Y$ and $y = Y$, and the image satisfies

$$Y = m(X - 2Y) + b$$

or $(1 + 2m)Y = mX + b$

This is the equation of a straight line, as required.

(b) Under the transformation, the four vertices have images as follows:

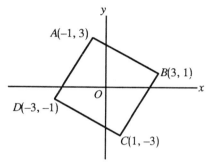

$$A(-1, 3) \rightarrow A'(5, 3)$$
$$B(3, 1) \rightarrow B'(5, 1)$$
$$C(1, -3) \rightarrow C'(-5, -3)$$
$$D(-3, -1) \rightarrow D'(-5, -1)$$

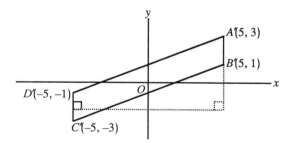

Since $A'B' = D'C' = 2$ and $A'B' \parallel C'D'$, $A'B'C'D'$ is a parallelogram.
Its base is $C'D' = 2$ and its height is 10, so its area is 20.

23. <u>Solution</u>

If n is composite, it has factors, say $n = ab$ where a and b are integers. Then

$$2^n - 1 = 2^{ab} - 1$$
$$= (2^a)^b - 1$$

By the Factor Theorem, $m^b - 1$ has factors, one of which is $m - 1$.
Hence, $(2^a)^b - 1$ has factors, one of which is $2^a - 1$.
Thus, $2^n - 1$ is composite if n is composite and so M_n is not a prime.
The first four Mersenne primes are 3, 7, 31, and 127.

24. Solution

    Since the rotation takes place at a constant speed, there will be equal intervals between
    the spots hit.

    Consequently, the first spot hit will also be the first spot hit for the second time.

    In one hour the number of hits is $\frac{3600}{275} = \frac{144}{11}$.

    Therefore, it will take 11 revolutions for the first spot to be hit for the second time.

    Hence, the number of hits in 11 revolutions is $\frac{144}{11} \times 11 = 144$.

    When the death ray has been fired 145 times, the same spot will be hit a second time.

25. Solution

    Let the lengths of the sides of the tiles be x and y with $x > y$.

    Then $nx^2 = (n + 76)y^2$

    $$x^2 = \left(\frac{n + 76}{n}\right)y^2$$

    Since x, y, and n are integers, $\frac{n + 76}{n}$ must be the quotient of two squares which
    differ by 76.

    Let these squares be p^2 and q^2.

    $p^2 - q^2 = 76$

    $(p - q)(p + q) = 76$

    This gives three possible systems of equations:

    $p + q = 76 \qquad p + q = 19 \qquad p + q = 38$
    $p - q = 1 \qquad\ p - q = 4 \qquad\ p - q = 2$

    The first two systems have no integer solutions.

    The third system has solution $p = 20$, $q = 18$ from which we obtain $n = q^2 = 324$ or
    $n + 76 = p^2 = 400$, so $n = 324$.

Challenge Problems

1. Solution

   (a) $\dfrac{a}{b} + \dfrac{c}{d} = \dfrac{a+c}{b+d}$

   $\dfrac{ad+bc}{bd} = \dfrac{a+c}{b+d}$

   $(ad+bc)(b+d) = bd(a+c)$

   $abd + ad^2 + b^2c + bcd = abd + bcd$

   $ad^2 = -b^2c$

   Since a, b, c, d are non-zero, $b^2 > 0$ and $d^2 > 0$.
   Hence, a and c are opposite in sign.
   Thus, $ac < 0$.

   (b) Since $\dfrac{a+c}{b+d} = 0$, $a + c = 0$ and $c = -a$.

   Thus, $\dfrac{a}{b} + \dfrac{c}{d} = \dfrac{a}{b} - \dfrac{a}{d} = 0$.

   Therefore, $\dfrac{a}{b} = \dfrac{a}{d}$, so $b = d$.

2. Solution

   (a) Flattening the cube out, as in the diagram, the astronaut can access three faces and on each of them can access an area equal to one-quarter of a circle with radius s. Hence, the surface area accessible is $\dfrac{3}{4}\pi s^2$.

   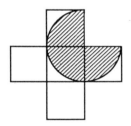

   (b) If the astronaut is at O, the area accessible is four times sector OAB plus eight times triangle OCA.

   Since $OA = OB = AB = s$, $\angle AOB = 60°$.
   Therefore, sector $OAB = \dfrac{1}{6}\pi s^2$.

   In $\triangle OCA$, the height is $\dfrac{s}{2}$ and the base AC

   is $XA - XC$ where $XA = \dfrac{\sqrt{3}}{2}s$ and

   $XC = \dfrac{s}{2}$.

   The area of $\triangle OCA$ is $\dfrac{1}{8}(\sqrt{3} - 1)s^2$.

   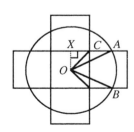

The total accessible area is

$$4\left(\tfrac{1}{6}\pi s^2\right) + 8\left[\tfrac{1}{8}(\sqrt{3}-1)s^2\right], \text{ or}$$

$$\left(\tfrac{2}{3}\pi + \sqrt{3} - 1\right)s^2.$$

3. Solution

Since r is a root of both equations, $r^2 - br + c = 0$ and $r^2 + br + d = 0$.

By subtracting these equations we obtain $r = \dfrac{c-d}{2b}$.

By adding the equations we obtain $r^2 = -\dfrac{c+d}{2}$.

From the properties of roots of quadratic equations,

$$r + r_1 = b \qquad (1)$$
$$rr_1 = c \qquad (2)$$
$$r + r_2 = -b \qquad (3)$$
$$rr_2 = d \qquad (4)$$

Using (1) and (3), $r_1 + r_2 = -2r$

$$= -\frac{c-d}{b}$$

Using (2) and (4), $r^2 r_1 r_2 = cd$ and $r_1 r_2 = \dfrac{cd}{r^2}$

$$= -\frac{2cd}{c+d}$$

The required equation is $x^2 - (r_1 + r_2)x + r_1 r_2 = 0$ or $x^2 + \dfrac{c-d}{b}x - \dfrac{2cd}{c+d} = 0$.

Now $r^2 = -\dfrac{c+d}{2}$ and $r^2 = \dfrac{(c-d)^2}{4b^2}$.

Hence, $\dfrac{2b^2}{(c-d)^2} = -\dfrac{1}{c+d}$

$$b^2 = -\frac{(c-d)^2}{2(c+d)}$$

If both c and d are positive, then b^2 is a negative number, and b cannot be a real number.

4. Solution

By dividing each term of the given equation by x^3, we get

$$d\left(\frac{y}{x}\right)^3 + c\left(\frac{y}{x}\right)^2 + b\left(\frac{y}{x}\right) + a = 0$$

Since $d \neq 0$, this equation is a cubic in $\dfrac{y}{x}$ and so has three roots p, q, and r.

Thus we may write the equation in factored form as

$$d\left(\frac{y}{x} - p\right)\left(\frac{y}{x} - q\right)\left(\frac{y}{x} - r\right) = 0$$

which is the equation of three straight lines $\dfrac{y}{x} - p = 0$, $\dfrac{y}{x} - q = 0$, and $\dfrac{y}{x} - r = 0$.

The slopes of these lines are p, q, and r, respectively.

Using the properties of the roots,

$$d(p + q + r) = -c$$
$$d(pq + pr + qr) = b$$
$$d(pqr) = -a$$

Now, if any two lines, say the first two, are perpendicular, then $pq = -1$.

Thus, $d(p + q + r) = -c$
$$-d + dr(p + q) = b$$
$$dr = a$$

Hence, $d(p + q) = -c - dr = -c - a$ and $-d + a(p + q) = b$.

Therefore, $-d + a\left(\dfrac{-c - a}{d}\right) = b$

$$-d^2 - ac - a^2 = bd$$
$$d^2 + ac + bd + a^2 = 0$$

5. Solution

The sum of an infinite geometric series with first term a and common ratio r, where $|r| < 1$, is $\dfrac{a}{1 - r}$.

Therefore, $S_n = \dfrac{a^n}{1 - r^n}$ for $n = 1, 2, 3, \dots$.

Hence,

$$\frac{1}{S_1} + \frac{1}{S_2} + \frac{1}{S_3} + \dots = \frac{1 - r}{a} + \frac{1 - r^2}{a^2} + \frac{1 - r^3}{a^3} + \dots$$

$$= \left(\frac{1}{a} + \frac{1}{a^2} + \frac{1}{a^3} + \dots\right) - \left(\frac{r}{a} + \frac{r^2}{a^2} + \frac{r^3}{a^3} + \dots\right)$$

$$= A - B$$

A is an infinite geometric series with first term $\dfrac{1}{a}$ and common ratio $\dfrac{1}{a}$.

Since $|a| > 1$, $\left|\dfrac{1}{a}\right| < 1$ and $A = \dfrac{\dfrac{1}{a}}{1 - \dfrac{1}{a}}$

$$= \frac{1}{a - 1}$$

B is an infinite geometric series with first term $\dfrac{r}{a}$ and common ratio $\dfrac{r}{a}$.

Since $|a| > 1$ and $|r| < 1$, then $\left|\dfrac{r}{a}\right| < 1$.

Thus, $B = \dfrac{\dfrac{r}{a}}{1 - \dfrac{r}{a}}$

$$= \frac{r}{a - r}$$

Therefore, $\dfrac{1}{S_1} + \dfrac{1}{S_2} + \dfrac{1}{S_3} + \dots = \dfrac{1}{a - 1} - \dfrac{r}{a - r}$

$$= \frac{a(1 - r)}{(a - 1)(a - r)}$$

6. Solution

    Since $\angle A$ is bisected, $\angle BAD = \angle DAC = 45°$.

    In $\triangle ADC$, $\dfrac{DC}{\sin 45°} = \dfrac{AD}{\sin C}$

    $$\sqrt{2}\,DC = \dfrac{AD}{\sin C}$$

    From $\triangle ABC$, $\sin C = \dfrac{AB}{BC} = \dfrac{c}{\sqrt{b^2 + c^2}}$

    Therefore, $\sqrt{2}\,DC = \dfrac{AD\sqrt{b^2 + c^2}}{c}$ \qquad (1)

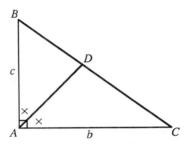

    Similarly, in $\triangle ADB$, $\dfrac{BD}{\sin 45°} = \dfrac{AD}{\sin B}$

    $$\sqrt{2}\,BD = \dfrac{AD\sqrt{b^2 + c^2}}{b} \qquad (2)$$

    Adding (1) and (2) gives $\sqrt{2}\,(DC + BD) = AD\sqrt{b^2 + c^2}\left(\dfrac{1}{c} + \dfrac{1}{b}\right)$

    $$= AD\sqrt{b^2 + c^2}\left(\dfrac{b + c}{bc}\right)$$

    But $DC + BD = BC = \sqrt{b^2 + c^2}$.

    Therefore, $\sqrt{2}\,\sqrt{b^2 + c^2} = AD\sqrt{b^2 + c^2}\left(\dfrac{b + c}{bc}\right)$.

    Hence, $AD = \dfrac{\sqrt{2}\,bc}{b + c}$.

7. Solution 1

    We let $k = x^2 + 1$, $k^2 = y^2 + 1$, both be members of S, and seek a contradiction.

    Then $y^2 + 1 = (x^2 + 1)^2$

    $$y^2 = x^4 + 2x^2$$
    $$= x^2(x^2 + 2)$$

    Then $\left(\dfrac{y}{x}\right)^2 = x^2 + 2$.

    Since $x^2 + 2$ is an integer, let $\left(\dfrac{y}{x}\right)^2 = z^2$, where z is an integer.

    Thus, $\quad z^2 = x^2 + 2$

    $\quad z^2 - x^2 = 2$

    But any two squares differ by at least 3 since

    $$(n + 1)^2 - n^2 = 2n + 1 \geq 3, \text{ for } n \geq 1.$$

    Hence, $z^2 - x^2 = 2$ is not possible.

    This is a contradiction, so k and k^2 cannot both be in S.

    Solution 2

    Let k and k^2 be in S.

    Then $k^2 = y^2 + 1$, as before.

Hence, $k^2 - y^2 = 1$, and so $(k - y)(k + y) = 1$.

Then $k - y = k + y = 1$, or $k - y = k + y = -1$.

A solution of the first case gives $k = 1$, $y = 0$, in the second case, $k = -1$, $y = 0$.

But $k > 1$, so there is no solution.

Again, this is a contradiction, and so k and k^2 cannot both be in S.

8. Solution

Let S and T be the centres of the smaller circles.

Join CS and DT.

Since an angle inscribed in a semicircle is a right angle, $\angle APB = \angle ACQ = \angle QDB = 90°$.

Since PA and PB are straight lines,

$\angle PCQ = \angle PDQ = 90°$.

Hence, $PCQD$ is a rectangle.

Now PQ and CD are the diagonals of the rectangle, so $MQ = MD$ and $\angle MQD = \angle MDQ$.

Since TQ and TD are equal radii, $\angle TQD = \angle TDQ$.

Also, since $PQ \perp AB$, $\angle MQD + \angle DQT = 90°$.

Therefore, $\angle TDQ + \angle MDQ = \angle MDT = 90°$.

Since TD is a radius and $\angle MDT = 90°$, CD is tangent to the circle with centre T.

By a similar argument, CD is tangent to the circle with centre S.

Thus, we conclude that CD is a common tangent to the two smaller semicircles.

9. Solution

For any value of y it is required that there be an x such that

$$y = \frac{a + 3x}{(x - 1)(x + 1)} = \frac{a + 3x}{x^2 - 1}.$$

Note that if $a = 3$, then $y = \frac{3}{x - 1}$ and there is no value of x for which $y = 0$.

If $a = -3$, then $y = \frac{3}{x + 1}$ and there is no value for x for which $y = 0$.

Therefore $a \neq -3$, $a \neq 3$.

If $y = \frac{a + 3x}{x^2 - 1}$, then $yx^2 - 3x - (a + y) = 0$.

If $y = 0$, then $x = -\frac{a}{3}$.

If $y \neq 0$, $x = \frac{3 \pm \sqrt{9 + 4y(a + y)}}{2y}$, $y \neq 0$.

Since x is real, the discriminant must be non-negative.

$9 + 4y(a + y) \geq 0$

$4y^2 + 4ay + 9 \geq 0$

This inequality will be true provided the discriminant is non-negative.

Thus, $16a^2 - 16(9) \leq 0$

$$a^2 \leq 9$$

$$-3 \leq a \leq 3.$$

But from above, $a \neq -3$, $a \neq 3$.

Therefore, $-3 < a < 3$.

10. Solution 1

Construct BD so that $\angle DBA = \angle CAB = x$.

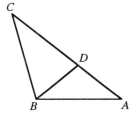

Since $\angle CDB$ is an exterior angle of $\triangle BDA$,

$\angle CDB = 2x = \angle CBD$.

Hence, $CD = CB = a$ and $DB = DA = b - a$.

Also, $\cos x = \dfrac{(b - a)^2 + c^2 - (b - a)^2}{2c(b - a)} = \dfrac{c}{2(b - a)}$.

Similarly, $\cos 2x = \dfrac{b - a}{2a}$.

Noting that $\cos 2x = 2\cos^2 x - 1$, we obtain

$$\frac{b - a}{2a} = 2\left(\frac{c^2}{4(b - a)^2}\right) - 1 = \frac{c^2 - 2(b - a)^2}{2(b - a)^2}$$

Therefore, $ac^2 - 2a(b - a)^2 = (b - a)^3$

$$ac^2 = (b^2 - a^2)(b - a)$$

Solution 2

Since $\angle C = \pi - 4A$, $\sin C = \sin(\pi - 4A) = \sin 4A$.

By the Law of Sines,

$$\frac{a}{\sin A} = \frac{b}{\sin 3A} = \frac{c}{\sin 4A} = k, \text{ where } k \text{ is a parameter.}$$

Hence, $ac^2 = (k \sin A)(k^2 \sin^2 4A)$

$$= k^3 \sin A \sin^2 4A$$

Now, $(b^2 - a^2)(b - a) = (b - a)^2(b + a)$

$$= k^3(\sin 3A - \sin A)^2(\sin 3A + \sin A)$$

$$= k^3(2 \cos 2A \sin A)^2(2 \sin 2A \cos A)$$

$$= k^3(2 \cos^2 2A)(2 \sin^2 A \cos A)(2 \sin 2A)$$

$$= k^3(2 \cos^2 2A)(\sin 2A \sin A)(2 \sin 2A)$$

$$= k^3 \sin A(2 \sin 2A \cos 2A)^2$$

$$= k^3 \sin A \sin^2 4A$$

Hence, $ac^2 = (b^2 - a^2)(b - a)$.

11. <u>Solution</u>

(a)   The coefficients of the given terms are $\left(\begin{array}{c} n \\ r-1 \end{array}\right), \left(\begin{array}{c} n \\ r \end{array}\right), \left(\begin{array}{c} n \\ r+1 \end{array}\right)$.

Since these are terms in an arithmetic sequence, $\left(\begin{array}{c} n \\ r \end{array}\right) - \left(\begin{array}{c} n \\ r-1 \end{array}\right) = \left(\begin{array}{c} n \\ r+1 \end{array}\right) - \left(\begin{array}{c} n \\ r \end{array}\right)$.

Using $\left(\begin{array}{c} n \\ r \end{array}\right) = \dfrac{n(n-1)\ldots(n-r+1)}{r!}$, we obtain

$$\frac{n(n-1)\ldots(n-r+1)}{r!} - \frac{n(n-1)\ldots(n-r+2)}{(r-1)!}$$

$$= \frac{n(n-1)\ldots(n-r)}{(r+1)!} - \frac{n(n-1)\ldots(n-r+1)}{r!}$$

Hence, $\dfrac{n-r+1}{r} - 1 = \dfrac{(n-r)(n-r+1)}{r(r+1)} - \dfrac{n-r+1}{r}$

$$n - 2r + 1 = \frac{1}{r+1}[(n-r+1)(n-2r-1)]$$

$$(n-2r)^2 = n+2$$

(b)   From (a), $(n-2r)^2 = n+2$ where n and r are integers.
Then, $4r^2 - 4nr + (n^2 - n - 2) = 0$

and $r = \dfrac{4n \pm \sqrt{16n^2 - 16n^2 + 16n + 32}}{8}$

$$= \frac{4n \pm 4\sqrt{n+2}}{8}$$

$$= \frac{n \pm \sqrt{n+2}}{2}$$

For r to be an integer, $\sqrt{n+2}$ must be an integer.
Hence, $n = k^2 - 2$, where k is an integer and $k \geq 2$.
Then, $r = \dfrac{k^2 - 2 \pm k}{2} = \dfrac{k^2 \pm k - 2}{2}$
Note that if $k = 2$, then $n = 2$ and $r = 2$ and so there is no $(r+1)$st term in the expansion.
Hence, $k \geq 3$ is required to meet the given conditions.
The pairs of positive integers (n, r) are $\left(k^2 - 2, \dfrac{k^2 \pm k - 2}{2}\right)$, where k is an integer greater than 2.

12. <u>Solution</u>

(a)   Assume that the result is false, and that every element occurs at least twice.
If there is an element a_1, then there are two such elements and between them there must be an element a_2, since no two like elements are adjacent.
Then the sequence is in the form

$$\ldots a_1 \ldots a_2 \ldots a_1 \ldots$$

Now, from condition (ii) a second a_2 cannot appear before the first a_1 nor after the second a_1, so there must be a nesting situation of the form

$$\ldots a_1 \ldots a_2 \ldots a_2 \ldots a_1 \ldots .$$

A similar argument leads to the conclusion that there must be two a_3's between the a_2's, two a_4's between the a_3's, and so on, creating an infinite chain of different symbols.

This is a contradiction, since only n elements are given, and we conclude that there must be some element x which occurs only once.

(b)   The sequence $1234\ldots(n-1)n(n-1)\ldots4321$ has length $2n-1$ and satisfies the given conditions.

13. <u>Solution 1</u>

For any i, $a_i - i \geq 0$ and hence $|a_i - i| = a_i - i$

or $a_i - i < 0$ and hence $|a_i - i| = i - a_i = a_i - i + 2(i - a_i)$.

Since $i - a_i$ is an integer, we can write every term as $a_i - i + 2u_i$ where $u_i = 0$ if $a_i - i \geq 0$ and otherwise is a positive integer sufficiently large to make $a_i - i + 2u_i \geq 0$.

$$\sum_{i=1}^{n} |a_i - i| = \sum_{i=1}^{n} a_i - \sum_{i=1}^{n} i + 2\sum_{i=1}^{n} u_i$$

Now, $\sum_{i=1}^{n} a_i = \sum_{i=1}^{n} i$ and $2\sum_{i=1}^{n} u_i$ is even, so $\sum_{i=1}^{n} |a_i - i|$ is always even.

<u>Solution 2</u>

Noting that $x \equiv -x \pmod 2$, we obtain

$$\sum_{i=1}^{n} |a_i - i| \equiv \sum_{i=1}^{n} (a_i - i) \pmod 2$$

$$\equiv \left[\sum_{i=1}^{n} a_i - \sum_{i=1}^{n} i \right] \pmod 2$$

$$\equiv 0 \pmod 2 \text{ since } \sum_{i=1}^{n} a_i = \sum_{i=1}^{n} i$$

Hence, $\sum_{i=1}^{n} |a_i - i|$ is always even.

14. <u>Solution</u>

Let n be the integral part of x and d be the decimal part.

Then $[x] = n$ and $x - [x] = d$.

Now consider three cases, $0 \leq d < \frac{1}{3}$, $\frac{1}{3} \leq d < \frac{2}{3}$, and $\frac{2}{3} \leq d < 1$.

Case 1

If $0 \le d < \frac{1}{3}$, then $[3x] = 3n$.

The equation $\frac{1}{[x]} + \frac{1}{[3x]} = x - [x]$ becomes

$$\frac{1}{n} + \frac{1}{3n} = d$$

$$\frac{4}{3n} = d$$

Therefore, $0 \le \frac{4}{3n} < \frac{1}{3}$.

Since $n > 0$, we get $3n > 12$ or $n > 4$.

Since $d = \frac{4}{3n}$, this leads to solutions of the form $x = n + \frac{4}{3n}$, $n > 4$; that is

$x = 5\frac{4}{15}, \ 6\frac{2}{9}, \ 7\frac{4}{21}, \ \dots \ .$

Case 2

If $\frac{1}{3} \le d < \frac{2}{3}$, then $[3x] = 3n + 1$.

The equation $\frac{1}{[x]} + \frac{1}{[3x]} = x - [x]$ becomes

$$\frac{1}{n} + \frac{1}{3n} = d$$

$$\frac{4n + 1}{3n^2 + n} = d$$

Therefore, $\frac{1}{3} \le \frac{4n + 1}{3n^2 + n} < \frac{2}{3}$.

Since $n > 0$, we multiply the inequality by $3(3n^2 + n)$ to get

$$3n^2 + n \le 12n + 3 < 6n^2 + 2n.$$

If $3n^2 + n \le 12n + 3$, $3n^2 - 11n - 3 \le 0$, which has the solution

$\frac{11 - \sqrt{157}}{6} \le n \le \frac{11 + \sqrt{157}}{6}$, or approximately $-0.255 \le n \le 3.922$.

Positive integers in this interval are $n = 1, 2,$ or 3.

If $12n + 3 < 6n^2 + 2n$, then $6n^2 - 10n - 3 > 0$, which has the solution

$n < \frac{10 - \sqrt{172}}{12} \approx -0.260$ or $n > \frac{10 + \sqrt{172}}{12} \approx 1.926$.

Positive integers in these intervals are $n = 2, 3, 4, 5, \dots \ .$

Thus the only integers satisfying both inequalities are $n = 2$ and $n = 3$.

Therefore $x = n + \frac{4n + 1}{3n^2 + n}$, $n = 2$, or $n = 3$. Hence, $x = 2\frac{9}{14}$ and $x = 3\frac{13}{30}$.

Case 3

If $\frac{2}{3} \le d < 1$, then $[3x] = 3n + 2$.

The equation $\frac{1}{[x]} + \frac{1}{[3x]} = x - [x]$ becomes

$$\frac{1}{n} + \frac{1}{3n + 2} = d$$

$$\frac{4n + 2}{3n^2 + 2n} = d$$

Therefore, $\frac{2}{3} \le \frac{4n + 2}{3n^2 + 2n} < 1$.

Since $n > 0$, we multiply the inequality by $3(3n^2 + 2n)$ to get

$$6n^2 + 4n \le 12n + 6 < 9n^2 + 6n.$$

If $6n^2 + 4n \le 12n + 6$, then $6n^2 - 8n - 6 \le 0$ or $3n^2 - 4n - 3 \le 0$ which has the

solution $\frac{4 - \sqrt{52}}{6} \le n \le \frac{4 + \sqrt{52}}{6}$ or approximately $-0.535 \le n \le 1.869$.

If $12n + 6 < 9n^2 + 6n$, then $9n^2 - 6n - 6 > 0$ or $3n^2 - 2n - 2 > 0$ which has the

solution $n < \frac{2 - \sqrt{28}}{6} \approx -0.549$ or $n > \frac{2 + \sqrt{28}}{6} \approx 1.215$.

There are no integers which satisfy both inequalities and so Case 3 yields no solutions.

Therefore, the complete solution is $x = 2\frac{9}{14}$, $x = 3\frac{13}{30}$ or $x = n + \frac{4}{3n}$, where n is an integer and $n > 4$.

15. Solution

The partition $n = 1 + 1 + \dots + 1$ is perfect for all values of n and hence there is at least one perfect partition. Suppose there is another perfect partition. Then it must have a largest element a where $a \ne 1$. Suppose a occurs r times in the partition. Now consider all smaller elements of the partition, say $b_1, \dots, b_j$.

We need to show that $b_1 + b_2 + \dots + b_j = a - 1$.

First note that if $b_1 + \dots + b_j < a - 1$, then $a - 1$ could not be represented as a sum of elements of the partition.

Hence, since the partition is perfect $b_1 + \dots + b_j \ge a - 1$.

Now suppose $b_1 + \dots + b_j > a - 1$ so that $b_1 + \dots + b_j = c$, where $c \ge a$.

Write $c = ma + d$, where $0 \le d \le a - 1$ and hence, $b_1 + \dots + b_j = ma + d$.

Now, since $d < a$, and the partition is perfect, there is a subset of $\{b_1, \dots, b_j\}$ whose sum is d. That is, $d = c_1 + \dots + c_k$.

But now $c = ma + c_1 + \dots + c_k$ can be represented in two ways as the sum of elements in the partition which is a contradiction.

Hence, $b_1 + b_2 + \dots + b_j = a - 1$.

Now consider the sum of all the elements in the partition
$$n = b_1 + \ldots + b_j + ra = (r+1)a - 1$$
or $n + 1 = (r+1)a$
If $n + 1$ is prime, this is impossible if $a > 1$ and so there is exactly one perfect partition.

16. Solution
Consider the graph of the equation $y = |2^j x - 1|$.
Note that $y = 2^j x - 1$ is a straight line with slope 2^j and x-intercept $\frac{1}{2^j}$.
Hence, $y = |2^j x - 1|$ is a piecewise linear function as shown below.

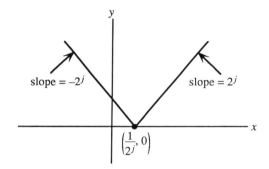

$S(x)$ is the sum of $n + 1$ such functions and so is piecewise linear.
The slope of $S(x)$ will change whenever the slope of one of the terms changes.
This occurs at $x = \frac{1}{2^n}, \frac{1}{2^{n-1}}, \ldots, 1$.
To the left of $x = \frac{1}{2^n}$ the slope of $S(x)$ is $-2^n - 2^{n-1} - \ldots - 1$ which is negative, so $S(x)$ is decreasing.
Between $\frac{1}{2^n}$ and $\frac{1}{2^{n-1}}$ the slope of $S(x)$ is
$$2^n - 2^{n-1} - 2^{n-2} - \ldots - 1 = 2^n - \left(\frac{2^n - 1}{1}\right) = +1.$$
Hence, $S(x)$ is increasing on this interval.
Similarly, to the right of $x = \frac{1}{2^{n-1}}$, $S(x)$ is increasing.
Thus, the minimum occurs at $x = \frac{1}{2^n}$.

The minimum value of $S(x)$ is

$$S\left(\frac{1}{2^n}\right) = \sum_{j=0}^{n} \left|\frac{2^j}{2^n} - 1\right|$$

$$= \sum_{j=0}^{n} \left(1 - \frac{2^j}{2^n}\right)$$

$$= n + 1 - \frac{2^{n+1} - 1}{2^n}$$

$$= n - 1 + \frac{1}{2^n}$$

17. Solution 1

Let the line l be the right bisector of AB.
Then the image of the point B in line l is
A and the image of the line BD is the line
AD'.

Since $\angle CAB = 60°$ and $\angle PBY = 120°$,
CAD' is a straight line.
Then the image of Y lies on this line, and
$XY = XP + PY'$.

Also, $\angle APX = \angle BPY = \angle APY'$, so PA is
the bisector of $\angle XPY'$ in $\triangle XPY'$.

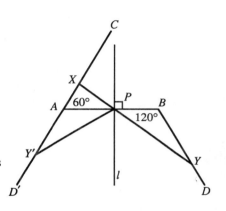

We prove the lemma:
The bisector of an angle of a triangle is
equal to or less than half the sum of the
arms of the angle.

Proof:

In $\triangle ABC$, let $AB = C$, $AC = b$, $AD = d$,
where AD is the bisector of $\angle BAC$.
By the angle bisector theorem, $BD = kc$
and $DC = kb$, where $0 < k < 1$ by the
triangle inequality theorem.

Since AD bisects $\angle BAC$,
$\cos \angle BAD = \cos \angle DAC$ and using the
Cosine Law we obtain

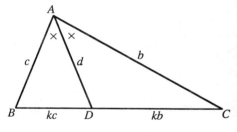

$$\frac{c^2 + d^2 - k^2 c^2}{2cd} = \frac{b^2 + d^2 - k^2 b^2}{2bd}$$

$$bc^2 + bd^2 - k^2 bc^2 = b^2 c + cd^2 - k^2 cb^2$$

$$(b - c)d^2 = bc(b - c) - k^2 bc(b - c)$$

$$d^2 = bc(1 - k^2)$$

Therefore, $d^2 \leq bc$.

By the arithmetic-geometric mean property, $\dfrac{b+c}{2} \geq \sqrt{bc}$.

Therefore, $d^2 \leq bc \leq \dfrac{(b+c)^2}{4}$, and so $d \leq \dfrac{b+c}{2}$.

Returning to the problem and employing this result, $XY = XP + PY' \geq 2AP = AB$.
Therefore, $XY \geq AB$.

Solution 2

Let $\angle AXP$ be θ.

Then $\angle APX = \angle BPY = 120° - \theta$, and $\angle PYB = \theta - 60°$.

Now $60° < \theta \leq 120°$, since if $\theta = 60°$, then XY is parallel to BD, and Y would not lie in BD, while if $\theta = 120°$, then XY becomes AB.

Using the Sine Law and $AP = PB = \frac{1}{2}AB$,

$$XP = \frac{\sin 60°}{\sin \theta} AP = \frac{\sqrt{3}}{2 \sin \theta} AP$$

$$PY = \frac{\sin 120°}{\sin (\theta - 60°)} AP = \frac{\sqrt{3}}{2 \sin (\theta - 60°)} AP$$

Therefore, $XY = \dfrac{\sqrt{3}}{4} AB \left[\dfrac{1}{\sin \theta} + \dfrac{1}{\sin (\theta - 60°)} \right]$

$$= \frac{\sqrt{3}}{4} AB \left[\frac{\sin (\theta - 60°) + \sin \theta}{\sin \theta \sin (\theta - 60°)} \right]$$

$$= \frac{\sqrt{3}}{4} AB \frac{2 \sin (\theta - 30°) \cos 30°}{\frac{1}{2} \left[\cos 60° - \cos (2\theta - 60°) \right]}$$

$$= \frac{\sqrt{3}}{4} AB \frac{2 \left(\frac{\sqrt{3}}{2} \right) \sin (\theta - 30°)}{\frac{1}{2} \left[\frac{1}{2} - \cos 2(\theta - 30°) \right]}$$

$$= AB \frac{3 \sin (\theta - 30°)}{1 - 2 \cos 2(\theta - 30°)}$$

$$= AB \frac{3 \sin (\theta - 30°)}{1 - 2 \left[1 - 2 \sin^2 (\theta - 30°) \right]}$$

$$= AB \frac{3 \sin (\theta - 30°)}{4 \sin^2 (\theta - 30°) - 1}$$

Replace $\theta - 30°$ by α.

Since $60° < \theta \le 120°$, then $30° < \alpha \le 90°$, and so $\frac{1}{2} < \sin \alpha \le 1$.

Hence, $4 \sin^2 \alpha - 1 > 1$.

Also $4 \sin \alpha + 1 > 0$, while $\sin \alpha - 1 \le 0$.

Thus, $(4 \sin \alpha + 1)(\sin \alpha - 1) \le 0$

$$4 \sin^2 \alpha - 1 \le 3 \sin \alpha$$

Therefore, $\dfrac{XY}{AB} = \dfrac{3 \sin \alpha}{4 \sin^2 \alpha - 1} \ge 1$

and so $XY \ge AB$, with equality only if $\alpha = 90°$, or $\theta = 120°$.

18. Solution

(a) $f(3, 2) = \begin{pmatrix} 3 \\ 0 \end{pmatrix}\begin{pmatrix} 5 \\ 3 \end{pmatrix} + \begin{pmatrix} 3 \\ 1 \end{pmatrix}\begin{pmatrix} 4 \\ 3 \end{pmatrix} + \begin{pmatrix} 3 \\ 2 \end{pmatrix}\begin{pmatrix} 3 \\ 3 \end{pmatrix}$

$\qquad\qquad = 10 + 12 + 3$

$\qquad\qquad = 25$

(b) $f(n, r) = \displaystyle\sum_{j=0}^{\infty} \begin{pmatrix} n \\ j \end{pmatrix}\begin{pmatrix} n + r - j \\ n \end{pmatrix}$

$\qquad\qquad = \displaystyle\sum_{j=0}^{\infty} \dfrac{n!}{(n-j)!\, j!} \dfrac{(n+r-j)!}{n!(r-j)!}$

$\qquad\qquad = \displaystyle\sum_{j=0}^{\infty} \dfrac{(n+r-j)!}{j!(n-j)!(r-j)!}$

$f(r, n) = \displaystyle\sum_{j=0}^{\infty} \begin{pmatrix} r \\ j \end{pmatrix}\begin{pmatrix} r + n - j \\ n \end{pmatrix}$

$\qquad\qquad = \displaystyle\sum_{j=0}^{\infty} \dfrac{r!}{j!(r-j)!} \dfrac{(n+r-j)!}{(n-j)!r!}$

$\qquad\qquad = f(n, r)$

(c) $f(n, n) = \displaystyle\sum_{j=0}^{\infty} \begin{pmatrix} n \\ j \end{pmatrix}\begin{pmatrix} 2n - j \\ n \end{pmatrix}$

$\qquad\qquad = \displaystyle\sum_{j=0}^{\infty} \begin{pmatrix} n \\ n-j \end{pmatrix}\begin{pmatrix} n + (n-j) \\ n-j \end{pmatrix}, \qquad$ using $\begin{pmatrix} n \\ j \end{pmatrix} = \begin{pmatrix} n \\ n-j \end{pmatrix}$

Now, for $j > n, \begin{pmatrix} n \\ j \end{pmatrix}$ is 0 and as j goes from 0 to n, $(n-j)$ goes from n to 0, so there is an exact correspondence of terms.

Hence, setting $n - j = \alpha$, we obtain $f(n, n) = \displaystyle\sum_{\alpha=0}^{\infty} \begin{pmatrix} n \\ \alpha \end{pmatrix}\begin{pmatrix} n + \alpha \\ \alpha \end{pmatrix}$.

(d) If the given statement is to be true, then it is also true that
$$f(a, b) - f(a, b-1) = f(a-1, b) + f(a-1, b-1).$$

Using the Pascal Identity $\binom{n}{k} + \binom{n}{k-1} = \binom{n+1}{k}$, and omitting the range of summation for brevity, we obtain

$$f(a, b) - f(a, b-1) = \sum \binom{a}{j}\binom{a+b-j}{a} - \binom{a}{j}\binom{a+b-j-1}{a}$$

$$= \sum \binom{a}{j}\binom{a+b-j-1}{a-1}$$

$$= \sum \left[\binom{a-1}{j} + \binom{a-1}{j-1}\right]\binom{a+b-j-1}{a-1}$$

$$= f(a-1, b) + \sum \binom{a-1}{j-1}\binom{a+b-j-1}{a-1}$$

Further, setting $j - 1 = k$,

$$\sum \binom{a-1}{j-1}\binom{a+b-j-1}{a-1} = \sum \binom{a-1}{k}\binom{a+b-k-2}{a-1}$$

$$= f(a-1, b-1)$$

Hence, $f(a, b) = f(a, b-1) + f(a-1, b) + f(a-1, b-1)$.

19. <u>Solution</u>

The first step in the solution is to prove that $\angle DEC$ is a maximum *if and only if* AB is tangent to the circle through C, D, and E.

Proof:

(i) Suppose AB is tangent at E and E' is any other point on AB.

Let E'' be the point of intersection of DE' and the circle through D, E, and C.

Then, $\angle DE''C = \angle DEC$. [angles subtended by the same arc]

Also $\angle DE''C > \angle DE'C$. [an exterior angle of a triangle is greater than an interior and opposite angle]

Therefore, $\angle DEC > \angle DE'C$ if AB is tangent to the circle through C, D, and E.

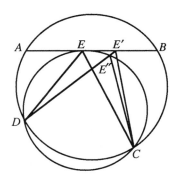

(ii)   Suppose *AB* is *not* tangent at *E*.
       By a similar argument to the one above,
       $\angle DE''C > \angle DE'C = \angle DEC$.
       Therefore, if *AB* is not tangent, $\angle DEC$
       is not a maximum.
       Thus $\angle DEC$ is a maximum if and only
       if *AB* is tangent.

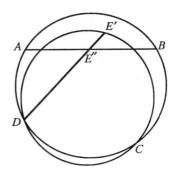

Now prove that *AB* is tangent to the circle through *C*, *D*, and *E* *if and only* if
$\angle ADE = \angle ECB$.

Proof:

(i)   Let the angles have the measures as
       indicated in the diagram.
       Since *BEC* is an angle between a chord
       and a tangent, then $\angle BEC = \angle EDC$; that
       is, $z = w$.
       Also, $y + z + v = 180°$. [opposite angles
       of cyclic quadrilateral *ABCD* have a sum
       of 180°]
       But in $\triangle EBC$, $x + w + v = 180°$.
       Since $z = w$, $x + z + v = 180°$.
       But $y + z + v = 180°$ and so $x = y$.
       Hence, $\angle ADE = \angle ECB$.

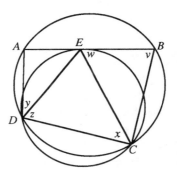

(ii) $y + z + v = 180°$ [opposite angles of cyclic quadrilateral *ABCD* have a sum of
       180°]
       In $\triangle EBC$, $w + x + v = 180°$.
       Therefore, $y + z = w + x$.
       But if $\angle ADE = \angle ECB$, then $z = w$.
       Therefore, *AEB* is tangent to the circle through *C*, *D*, and *E*. [angle between
       a tangent and a chord]
       Thus, $\angle DEC$ is a maximum if and only if $\angle ADE = \angle ECB$.

20. <u>Solution</u>

This solution uses the fact that $-\frac{2}{3} = \frac{1}{3} - \frac{3}{3}$, $-\frac{2}{6} = \frac{1}{6} - \frac{3}{3}\left(\frac{1}{2}\right)$, $-\frac{2}{9} = \frac{1}{9} - \frac{3}{3}\left(\frac{1}{3}\right)$, etc.

$\frac{p}{q} = 1 + \frac{1}{2} - \frac{2}{3} + \frac{1}{4} + \frac{1}{5} - \frac{2}{6} + \frac{1}{7} + \frac{1}{8} - \frac{2}{9} + \dots + \frac{1}{478} + \frac{1}{479} - \frac{2}{480}$

$= 1 + \frac{1}{2} + \frac{1}{3} + \frac{1}{4} + \frac{1}{5} + \frac{1}{6} + \dots + \frac{1}{480} - \frac{3}{3}\left(1 + \frac{1}{2} + \frac{1}{3} + \dots + \frac{1}{160}\right)$

$= \frac{1}{161} + \frac{1}{162} + \frac{1}{163} + \dots + \frac{1}{479} + \frac{1}{480}$

Grouping the first and last terms and continuing in pairs, we obtain

$\frac{p}{q} = \left(\frac{1}{161} + \frac{1}{480}\right) + \left(\frac{1}{161} + \frac{1}{479}\right) + \dots + \left(\frac{1}{320} + \frac{1}{321}\right)$

$= \frac{641}{161 \cdot 480} + \frac{641}{161 \cdot 479} + \frac{641}{162 \cdot 478} + \dots + \frac{641}{320 \cdot 321}$

$= 641\left(\frac{1}{161 \cdot 480} + \frac{1}{161 \cdot 479} + \dots + \frac{1}{320 \cdot 321}\right)$

$= \frac{641M}{161 \cdot 162 \cdot 163 \cdots 479 \cdot 480}$, where M is the accumulation of all numerators when the

fractions are brought to common denominators.

Now 641 is a prime and is therefore divisible only by 1 and 641. The denominator contains no factor of 641 and hence the numerator contains 641 with no simplification allowing for it to be removed.

Hence, 641 is a factor of p.